# YOUNIVERSE

A Short Guide to
Modern Science

# YOUNIVERSE

## A Short Guide to Modern Science

What are you? Who are you?
Where are you going?

Elsie Burch Donald

DUCKWORTH

First published in 2021 by Duckworth,
an imprint of Duckworth Books Ltd

1 Golden Court, Richmond,
TW9 1EU, United Kingdom

www.duckworthbooks.co.uk

### Illustration credits

Mark Brightman: pages xii, 156
John Woodcock: figures 1–12
AlisaRed/Shutterstock: page 70
Usagi-P/Shutterstock.com: page 126 (skull diagram)
Ramil Sitdikov/Sputnik/Science Photo Library: page 170 (Sophia)
Philippe Psaila/Science Photo Library: page 172 (Nao)

Internal design by Danny Lyle

ISBN: 978-0-7156-5422-4

# CONTENTS

# AUTHOR'S NOTE

*YOUNIVERSE* is a short introduction to the basics of modern science. It's also a travel guide. It describes in simple terms the world you are inseparably a part of: what it is, how it works and, most importantly, your place in it – insofar as these things are known. It's the book I wished for when I first made this journey myself.

The Big Bang, matter, energy, particle physics, biology, evolution and the future of technology are the subjects. Plain speech, short chapters, digestible chunks of information, absence of scientific terms and equations are the style.

Science is a realm of marvels. You are going to travel through time and space – a world of the unimaginably big and the inconceivably small. So it's important to take your time. The book is short, but the universe can't be swallowed in a day. The information is, I hope, clear cut, but as with any travel guide, there's a lot of it, and some bits may need review, if they are going to stick.

Our brains are filters. Faced with new input they can balk like a skittish pony refusing a jump, or slam shut like a clam. So here's a tip. Best to digest a chapter at a time. If something seems difficult, take a break and make another run at it. Maybe read the bare-bones summary at the end of the chapter, then read the 'difficult' bit again. Suddenly the fog will lift and it's perfectly clear. The words haven't changed, but your brain has. Rereading has allowed it to lay down references, find some connections and ready itself to fit in brand new material.

All the chapters have been vetted by distinguished professionals in each field and any errors are my own. My aim has been to present the topics clearly, and to smooth the reader's path by making them accessible and also entertaining. I enjoyed researching and writing this book enormously. I hope it shows, and that it's infectious.

# PREFACE

In the beginning, some 14 billion years ago, there was a massive 'explosion' and the universe was created – or, more precisely, it became a work in progress. Some cosmologists believe that this event, the Big Bang as it's called, wasn't unique. Rather it was one of several sequential big bangs, as one universe succeeded another, like a series of exploding Russian dolls. Our universe is merely the current one, or possibly one amongst many in a vast incomprehensible multiverse. Others think the universe may have been reborn – so having previously existed it collapsed in on itself, then rose again like a reseeded plant or indomitable bouncing ball. A few claim it popped out of a Black Hole, while a number maintain God's finger was on the trigger, firing once or repeatedly over time.

Although scientists are conflicted over these first micro-fractions of a second, they generally agree the Big Bang released an infinitesimal hyper-dense concentration of energy and matter that, over billions of years, clumped together to form the stars, planets and galaxies of our universe, and eventually ourselves.

A short account of how this happened, the structure of stars and matter, the mysterious arrival of life and emergence of human beings, the interconnectedness of all things on the planet, and your place in it, is, as has been noted, the subject of this book.

Why bother, people often wonder. It's hard enough to keep track of everyday news and goings-on. There's just more information around today than we can possibly assimilate. Renaissance man knew most of what there was to know because it wasn't much. We have to rely on experts: doctors for our bodies, psychiatrists and neurologists for our brains, mechanics for our cars, computer gurus for electronic devices, and astronauts, cosmologists and sci-fi for outer space. The only expertise we lack and really long for is a robotic domestic staff.

Having bought this book, however, you may feel differently. You may be curious. We humans are by nature pattern-makers and puzzle-solvers. Curiosity and wonder are innate; so is the desire to learn. What's more, we like to influence, even dominate our surroundings, animate and inanimate, and to chatter, sometimes responsibly, about debated issues. The more adventurous young may yearn for daring undertakings and new worlds to discover, even conquer. Science is where that territory lies.

Would you move into a house with no idea what it is made of or how the things inside it work, as an insect or a mouse might do? The universe houses you in one tiny corner. You are made of its material. You are 100 per cent dependent on it for food, warmth, light and body repairs. Every few years your body is replaced by new material from the universe, which with uncanny accuracy is customised and fitted into place, following a pattern dictated by your genes. You are a cell in the universal fabric. And when you die, you'll be absorbed back into the universe.

But right now, amazingly, you are quasi-separated from the universal blend. You are *you*, able to have a look around, take in the protean world you are a part of, possibly make some changes to it and at the same time learn something of what you are, who you are and where on earth you and your genes are going. You have five senses and the precious gift of consciousness with which to make the most of life, while you can.

# What Are You?

# 1

# GENESIS

*'It is the stars, the stars above us, govern our
conditions.'*         Shakespeare, *King Lear*

Some 13.8 billion years ago the future universe was a tiny speck, a fraction of the size of a nuclear particle. It was densely packed and incredibly hot. Suddenly out of this over-heated nano-egg burst a fireball that, in the blink of an eye, had doubled in size 100 times or more and created the basic building materials for every object in the universe, as well as time and space.

Within one 10,000th of a second after the Big Bang, when the ballooning fireball's temperature began to fall, the universe had become a chaotic mass of seething radiation (light) and subatomic particles colliding and annihilating each other in a violent particle war that lasted for the next 380,000 years.

By then, things having simmered down to about the temperature of the sun's surface today, the tiny warring particles could begin to stabilise and come together. The stars and planets began to form.

## STARS

The first stars appeared some 200 million years after the Big Bang. They were formed inside dense clouds of hydrogen gas and dust, the primordial soup of the early universe. Their evolution took millions of years, but within a few minutes of the Big Bang, vast clumps of hydrogen gas were being squashed into balls of helium by the pull of gravity. The process releases, as a kind of exhaust, energy in the form of heat and light. This is nuclear fusion. It keeps stars hot and shining. It can also make nuclear bombs.

Stars keep their stability by balancing the outward push of nuclear energy and the inner pull of gravity. But when the hydrogen that fuels a star runs short, the star begins to lose its balance. Eventually gravity wins and the star collapses in on itself or, if it's really big, explodes.

The earliest stars were truly gigantic – hundreds of times bigger than our sun. But being unstable they were comparatively short-lived – and hugely beneficial. Most of the elements in the universe were cooked inside them. When they exploded, they spewed out the building materials for generations of new stars, plus the essential *carbon*, *nitrogen*, *oxygen* and *iron* inside you and everything around you.

Stars are the mothers of the universe. You too are stardust.

Our **sun** is one of a 100 billion stars in the Milky Way galaxy. Some 5 billion years ago, clouds of hydrogen and dust, spinning faster and faster under gravity, flattened into a disc. Most of the material, 'gravitating' towards the centre, combined as described above to make the sun. The remaining material, swirling around the baby star, became the planets, moons and asteroids. Too small to be light-producing, they settled for a reflective glory.

Today, the sun's molten core is roughly the same temperature as the universe when a few minutes old. Much of what goes on inside it is also the same. Nuclear fusion keeps the gases hot and under enormous pressure. This releases radiation in the form of light. Light takes thousands of years to get from the sun's core to its surface. A lot of dodging and crashing about happens en route. But once the rays break free, they reach the earth, 150 million kilometres away, in only eight minutes.

Our sun has already used up half its hydrogen fuel. This means it's halfway through its lifespan. Once it can no longer keep up its hydrogen-versus-gravity balancing act, it will implode. When this happens, its contents will be dumped back into space and recycled to make new stars. But no one will be around to see it.

# ENIGMA

In 1998 an extraordinary discovery was made. Cosmologists suddenly observed that the universe was expanding, *really* fast. What's more, the *rate* of expansion was accelerating, the galaxies growing further and further apart. In short, gravity wasn't doing its job: things were flying apart instead of pulling together. Scientists were confounded. Could some other, stronger force or governor be at work? Nobody had a clue. Yet something was overpowering the dominant force of gravity.

Dubbed *dark energy*, the mysterious force joined an earlier proposal of an equally mysterious *dark matter*, which, giving out no light, was invisible. Just as dark energy may account for the universe flying apart, dark matter may have helped to pull it together in the first place.

Names make us feel more in control. But the fact remains that in spite of all we've discovered about the universe so far: its trillions of stars and galaxies – what they are made of, how they tick and so much more – something strange and utterly different is out there. And it's enormous.

As a result, the universe's composition has been radically revised: 73% is deemed to be dark energy and 23% dark matter. In other words, only 5% of the universe is known to us. As we are ourselves made of ordinary matter, dark energy and dark matter are for now beyond us in every sense.

## To summarise:

- The known universe is 3/4 hydrogen and 1/4 helium. However, only 5% of the whole universe is known to us.

- Stars are hydrogen-fueled nuclear furnaces. Most of the elements in the universe were cooked inside them over millions of years.

- When a star dies, its heat-forged elements spill out into the universe and are recycled.

- Stars created each other and almost everything in the universe, including you.

- Dark energy and dark matter make up most of the universe. Recently, dark matter's presence was 'mapped' by bouncing starlight off it. We still don't know what it is.

# 2

# MATTER AND MORTAR

*'Bishop Berkeley said there was no matter, so there was no matter what he said.'*     Lord Byron

If Bishop Berkeley had a viable point, it wasn't exactly the one that he was making. (But we'll get back to that.) Matter as we know it means the stuff of every known thing in the universe: microbes, insects, plants, animals, people, machines, mountains, oceans, planets, galaxies – everything that is physical. Matter is material. It's anything that has mass and occupies space. But what is that, when there are so many different kinds?

In the fourth century BC, the Greek philosopher Democritus divined that everything in the universe was made from combinations of a single indivisible grain. He named it *atomos*: indivisible. (He may have picked the idea up when visiting India.[1]) Atoms, said Democritus, had no

---

[1] The concept, attributed to the Hindu sage Aruni, appears in Upanishad texts from 800 BCE.

quality other than shape. They continually pushed and pulled each other about and joined up in different ways to make different things. They were like an alphabet, where joining the same letters up in different ways produces myriad stories and expressions.

Two thousand years later, in a brilliant piece of mathematical thinking, the young Albert Einstein confirmed Democritus' theory. Everything was indeed composed of tiny particles that form the basic building blocks of the universe.

That was in 1905. Since then we've had a closer look, and although atoms remain the universal building blocks, they are not in fact indivisible. We now know that every atom is composed of *three subatomic particles*: **protons**, **neutrons** and **electrons**. The protons and neutrons are bound together in a tight central *nucleus*, as shown (p. 8). They are themselves composed of three even tinier particles called **quarks**. Electrons, lightweight but hugely significant outliers, surround the atomic nucleus.

Atoms normally contain an equal number of protons, neutrons and electrons.

# Atom

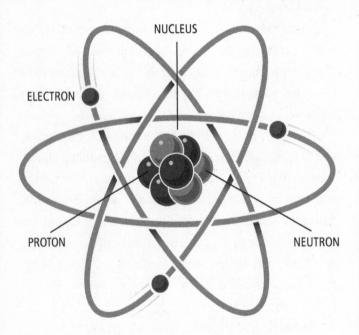

**Figure 1** An atom, the basic building block of matter, consists of a nucleus surrounded by electron particles.

The atomic world is micro-minuscule. An average atom's width is 100,000 times thinner than a human hair. And in case you're wondering, an estimated 5 million million hydrogen atoms can fit on the head of a pin. What's more, if an atom were magnified to the size of a football field, its nucleus would be the size of a pea. Unlike football stadiums, however, atoms are 99.9% empty space.

Most importantly, atoms have an *electrical* aspect. Protons are positively charged, electrons are negatively charged. Neutrons, as the name suggests, are neutral. They add mass. Since positive and negative charges cancel each other out, the atom itself is neutral and, therefore, *stable*. It can interact with other atoms and larger structures can be built.

All atomic building blocks need mortar to hold them together. This is the job of **four fundamental forces** (believed to have appeared in the Big Bang).

And that's it. Basically, every thing on earth is an assembly of three quarks and some flighty electrons held together by four fundamental forces. That's you in melt-down. Built up, however, your body consists of several billion, billion, billion atoms, all of which, remember, are 99.9% empty. And most of them are replaced every year.

# BUILDING MATTER FROM SCRATCH

How can a few simple particles account for the complexities of a human body, let alone every object in the Universe?

It works like this. Atoms come in different types. A collection of one type of atom is called an **element**. Its *number of protons* determines what element the atom is, and therefore what material it will make. For example, if an atom has 6 protons it's a carbon atom, so it builds carbon material: diamonds are pure carbon. If an atom has 7 protons it's nitrogen, and 8 protons it's oxygen.

There are 118 known elements in all. Each has its own name, mass and size, and all are arranged according to their number of protons in a list called the periodic table, which is every chemist's bible.

Your body is made of zillions of atoms, but only some 40 elements. As described in Chapter 1, these were pressure-cooked in stars 5 billion years ago and released into space when the stars exploded. They entered your body mainly through breathing, eating plants, and eating animals that have eaten plants.

A bonded group of *different* elements produces what is sensibly called a **compound**. Carbon dioxide is an example. Each molecule has 1 carbon and 2 oxygen atoms (written $CO_2$). Elements and compounds build all matter.

## A closer look

Matter has three states: solid, liquid and gas. Three features are crucial in building it: the *four fundamental forces*, mentioned above, *chemical bonding* (glue) and the bizarre, hugely important but crazy behaviour of *electrons*.

# THE FOUR FUNDAMENTAL FORCES

The four fundamental forces drive the universe. Each has a 'chariot particle' to carry it around.

The **strong nuclear force** holds the atom's quarks and its nucleus together. It's thousands of times stronger than gravity – at extremely short distances. Its chariot-carrying particle is called a *gluon*. Only quarks and gluons feel the strong force.

The **weak nuclear force** affects all matter. It helps fuse hydrogen to make helium in the sun. (Doing so, by the way, releases tiny particles called *neutrinos*. Billions are passing through your body as you read this.) The weak force also contributes to things falling apart (see *radioactive decay*, page 196). It's carried by particles called W and Z *bosons*.

The **electromagnetic force** combines all the electrical and magnetic forces. It keeps electrons inside atoms and helps link atoms to make larger structures. It's carried by *photons*, the basic units of light.

**Gravity**, the most familiar force, pulls bulk matter together. It caused the stars and planets to form and the reputed apple to fall on its discoverer Isaac Newton's head. Its chariot particle, the *graviton*, is in fact theoretical, having so far never been sighted. If it doesn't exist, it could seriously upset theoretical physics.

**Chemical bonds** glue atoms together. The job is done by flibbertigibbet electrons. So, before proceeding, let's take a look at these pivotal subatomic particles.

**Electrons** are almost beyond belief. The little critters are virtually weightless. They are only .01% of an atom's mass, they have no measurable position and they only show themselves, or arguably even exist, when interacting. Yet we know quite a bit about them, and their behaviour is crucial to chemistry, biology and the diversity of matter.

Continuously in motion, even spinning in more than one direction at the same time, so it's claimed, electrons inhabit so-called 'clouds'. These surround the nucleus, at fixed distances, rather like planets orbiting the earth. Each cloud has a particular energy level and holds the number of electrons suited to the atom's element. Only the electrons located in the cloud furthest from the atom's nucleus – the outermost or *valence* electrons – are involved in bonding.

# CHEMICAL BONDS

Chemical bonds have two main types: *covalent* and *ionic*.

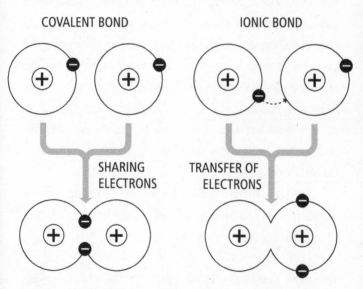

**COVALENT BOND**         **IONIC BOND**

**SHARING ELECTRONS**     **TRANSFER OF ELECTRONS**

**Figure 2** Covalent bonds are made by two atoms sharing an electron. Ionic bonds are made by transferring electrons from one atom to another. The black circles represent electrons, which are negatively charged.

**Covalent bonds** build both elements and compounds. They occur when two atoms, each one *sharing* an electron, make an overlapping bond, as shown in the diagram.

A **molecule** is an element or compound of atoms *joined by a covalent bond*.

**Ionic bonds** are made by *transferring* electrons from one atom to another, as shown. This builds **ionic compounds** (ionic compounds are never molecules). But what is an **ion**? It's an atom with a different number of electrons to protons – hence electrically charged, and unstable. But the advantage is, since opposite charges attract, other ions are keen to bond with it. This facilitates building matter. An atom's readiness to rearrange its bits to form molecules and ionic compounds makes an endless variety of new materials possible.

To recap: matter is built by joining the same type of atoms together to make an *element*. Or by joining different elements together to make a *compound*.

**Bondage**: before new bonds can form, the old ones must be broken up. This uses energy stored in the bonds themselves. But – and this is important – breaking a bond can release more energy than is needed to remake it. Suddenly, free energy is available for other uses, as you'll see in the next chapter.

## To summarise:

- Four fundamental forces, carried by special chariot particles, govern the universe.

- Atoms, the basic building blocks of matter, are composed of three quarks and some swirling electrons.

- A stable atom is electronically neutral. It has no charge.

- Atoms come in different types called elements, defined by their proton numbers. Most elements were cooked in stars, billions of years ago.

- When *different* types of atoms are joined, they make a compound.

- Atoms are joined by chemical bonds. This involves giving, taking or sharing electrons with another atom.

- Breaking a bond can release free energy.

- Chemical bonding of elements and compounds enables the build-up of all known materials and creates the possibilities for new ones.

# 3

# MOVERS AND SHAKERS

*'What goes up must come down.'*

(Attributed to Sir Isaac Newton)

In 1513, coming upon the Pacific Ocean, Vasco Nunez de Balboa waded right in and claimed the new-found sea for Spain. This sounds barmy, or at best an overzealous wish to curry favour with his powerful king. But Balboa knew that seas are valuable. They provide food and also roads that never need repair. And had he not completely lost his head, this indefatigable conquistador may have thought of looting China next. But decapitation intervened.

Balboa was an exceptionally energetic man, and the Pacific Ocean is, despite its name, an exceptionally energetic ocean. That animate and inanimate things should both possess energy may give pause. That every object in the universe, even a stone, possesses it, can beggar belief. But it is so.

# ENERGY

Energy is defined as the ability to do work – to cause movement and to make things happen. In that respect, it's a mental construct. And with a bit of thought you might have reached the same conclusion. But there is more to it than that.

First, energy cannot be created or destroyed; it is conserved forever. This is a law of nature.

Second, energy is interchangeable. It's an invisible shape-shifter capable of taking several forms, which can be *transferred* and/or *transformed* from one into another.

Chemical, radiant (light), thermal (heat), mechanical, electric and nuclear energies are all familiar terms. But overall, energy has two basic categories: **kinetic** (moving) energy and **potential** (stored) energy. Every object has both.

Here's an example. The food stored in your body contains *potential energy*. When you use some of it to move about it becomes *kinetic energy*. If you kick a ball, your kinetic energy is transferred to the ball. As the ball goes through the air, friction causes it to lose some energy. When it stops, any energy left in the ball is stored as potential energy, until it hits something else.

There are swings and roundabouts as energy moves from one place to another, often changing form en route. For instance: corn eaten by a chicken is stored as potential energy for the chicken to move and grow. If you eat the chicken, its meat is broken down by your digestion and stored as potential energy for *you* to move and grow.

While this is going on you breathe in oxygen and exhale carbon dioxide. The carbon dioxide is absorbed by plants, e.g. the corn.

With the help of chlorophyll and water, the sun's rays (**solar energy**) shining on the corn's leaves, converts the carbon dioxide into **chemical energy**, so that the corn can grow – and provide more chicken feed. During this process, called *photosynthesis*, the corn releases, as waste, the oxygen you inhale to stay alive.

All the energy stored in your body comes from plants, or animals that have eaten plants. It began as solar energy formed by nuclear reactions in the sun's core at least 100,000 years ago.

Plants are the go-betweens. Their direct link with the sun makes them arguably the most important living things on earth. They, almost uniquely, make their own food. All other living creatures depend on them for oxygen and food. In short, for life.

# A closer look

Balboa's energy, like ours and the chicken's, was **chemical energy**. Chemical energy is stored as potential energy in the bonds of molecules and compounds, described in the previous chapter.

The Pacific Ocean's energy comes straight from the sun, as **solar energy**. The sun's rays can warm the water's surface and the temperature difference between surface water and the cooler water beneath causes friction that releases **thermal** (heat) **energy**. In the tropics this is potentially powerful stuff. It's been said that only a small percentage of the energy trapped in oceans could one day power the world.

Today, the oceans' waves are used by power plants to make the **mechanical energy** that generates the **electrical energy** to light your house and run your computer, dishwasher and TV.

Many forms of energy – electrical, for instance – need a conductor to carry it. Others, like radiant (light) energy, don't need to hitch a ride. Light travels through space independent of matter.

**Heat energy** (originally from the sun) is the transfer or flow of energy between two systems, usually from a lower to a higher temperature. Heating and cooling allows matter to change states. But melting, boiling, freezing or evaporating, its atoms remain the same.

Heat is produced by molecules jiggling about. This causes friction. The more space between molecules, the more they're able to jiggle and the hotter a material gets.

Solids, liquids and gases have different energy levels, owing to how tightly or loosely their molecules are packed. Gases have the highest energy level of the three. Their molecules, being the most loosely organised, have the most jiggle room.

And something else: when you burn wood in a fireplace, its stored, potential energy is converted into three new forms: heat, sound and light (warmth, crackle and brightness). A small pile of ash remains.

But *mass*, like energy, is conserved. Query: what happened to the rest of the mass? Answer: it went up in smoke. That is to say, it became carbon dioxide gas and water vapour. Only the bits that failed to burn remained as ash.

Behaviour like this caused the young Albert Einstein, mulling it over at the nuclear level, to reach an extraordinary and mind-boggling conclusion. If two *atomic nuclei* were fused together, they too would end up with less mass than they had when separate. So what, in this case, would have happened to the missing mass?

It must have become energy, Einstein concluded. *Matter and energy must be interchangeable – they must be different forms of the same thing.*

Einstein expressed it succinctly in his famous equation: $E=mc^2$. Energy equals mass, times the speed of light multiplied by itself. As the speed of light is 186,000 miles per second, the available energy in an atomic nucleus is something humongous – billions of times stronger than the chemical energy that breaks up molecules. Bang!

Radical ideas about matter were nothing new, of course. In the eighteenth century, Bishop Berkeley (mentioned earlier, as lampooned by Byron) had declared that matter wasn't *real*. He claimed material objects were creations of the eye and mind. (Plato and others had thought something similar.) 'To be is to be perceived,' said Berkeley. But the question then arose, if no one was looking at an object did it cease to exist? The philosopher-bishop dug himself out of that hole by saying God could see it – provoking further mockery in the limerick verses below (attributed to the theologian Ronald Knox).

There once was a man who said, 'God
Must find it exceedingly odd
If he finds that this tree
Continues to be
When there's no one about in the quad.'

'Dear Sir: Your astonishment's odd;
I am always about in the quad.
And that's why the tree
Will continue to be
Since observed by, Yours faithfully, God.'

Suddenly, matter was energy and vice versa. Atoms formed everything but they were always in flux. Every few years the stuff of human bodies was replaced. If energy was a construct, mightn't matter be as well, just as Bishop Berkeley had presumed?

The distinguished twentieth-century physicists, Niels Bohr and Werner Heisenberg, claimed that indeed matter wasn't real. Their eminent colleague Erwin Schrodinger claimed that indeed it was. Both views would become acceptable. Reality was experiencing its biggest shake-up since Isaac Newton laid down the laws of gravity and motion in the seventeenth century. Quantum physics had arrived.

## To summarise:

- Energy is defined as the ability to do work. It has two categories: stored (potential) and moving (kinetic).

- Energy has several forms which can be *transferred* and/or *transformed*, one into another.

- Energy can be released from matter by breaking chemical bonds and by nuclear reactions.

- Energy and matter in the universe are conserved and interchangeable.

NB: If you've managed to get a grip on these three chapters – and it may take a bit of reviewing – you will know basically what matter is and how it's built up and energised to create every physical thing in the universe.

# 4

# ANOTHER WORLD

*'There are more things in heaven and earth, Horatio, than are dreamt of in your philosophy.'*

Shakespeare, *Hamlet*

Isaac Newton discovered that laws existed which governed the universe, and a force called gravity gave us a firm footing in it. Einstein saw things very differently. With imaginative, X-ray-like vision he perceived a universe beyond all sense perceptions. Its bizarre features would spark a rethink of the universe's nature that has continued ever since.

'Reality is merely an illusion, albeit a very persistent one,' Einstein once wryly observed. But unlike the reaction to Bishop Berkeley's rather similar notion, this time there was no lampooning. Einstein's insights and predictions have on the whole proved accurate.

Despite its revolutionary features, Einstein's world was generally an orderly one, with laws that guaranteed certain things always happened, given the same circumstances. But he was in for a shock. Pursuing the thread of his developing theories, he came upon a strange and wholly unexpected door. Naturally Einstein unlocked it. To his astonishment, he found he'd uncovered a madhouse: a topsy-turvy, seething micro-universe of mayhem, the wonderland of **quantum mechanics**. Einstein was incredulous. He couldn't – wouldn't – believe it. But today it is the norm.

Before taking a look, let's gaze for a moment at the great pillars of science Einstein's labours erected, and upon which all that followed was built.

A story goes that the French poet, Paul Valéry, meeting Einstein at a drinks party, asked the great man how he managed to keep track of his ideas. Did he carry a notebook, did he have a mnemonic system, did he scribble them hurriedly on his cuff – what was his method? Because, said Valéry, he faced that problem himself.

Einstein looked shyly down at his feet, then after a short pause answered, 'I've only had two ideas.'

This modest reference was, first, to his idea that *photons* (light), which carry the electromagnetic force, aren't waves but particles (for which he eventually received the

Nobel Prize). The second idea appeared in a theoretical paper, 'Special Relativity', published in 1905. As the word 'relativity' implies, it contained the destabilising predictions that, together with its follow-up, 'General Relativity' (1915), would quake Newtonian terra firma. Both papers defied all common sense, and still do.

In brief: *special relativity* is about space and time, while *general relativity* is about gravity.

Einstein declared that time and motion are *relative*. Objects only move in relation *to* other objects. So, movement depends on viewpoint – where you're placed or how you're moving in relation to another object, or it to you. A visual thinker, Einstein used thought experiments to reach his unique conclusions. As a boy he'd imagined racing a light beam. If both were running at the same speed, then he wouldn't know he was moving. If he was sitting on a train in the station and the train alongside moved forward, he would think it was his train that had moved.

But Einstein found one constant: the speed of light. At 186,000 miles per second, nothing could beat it. He further declared that mass and energy are interchangeable (as we have seen) and, of crucial significance, ditto space and time (see below). Then, having unified space and time, he redefined gravity, with a theory triggered by the thought that a man in free fall wouldn't feel his own weight.

At the heart of **relativity theory** is time and space. Einstein declared the two were intertwined. The result, **spacetime**, has *four* dimensions: the usual three for space, plus one for time. Einstein said spacetime's fabric was like a smooth rubber sheet and the sun was an iron ball that, dropped on to the sheet, causes a trough around it (see Figure 3, p. 28). He said all objects distort spacetime in this way. The 'warping' or unevenness of spacetime's smooth fabric is what enables unfuelled objects to move in space. In other words, spacetime is distorted by the presence of matter, and the distortion allows matter to move.

Now, wherever there is matter there is gravity, as we know. Gravity pulled matter together in the first place. But **gravity**, said Einstein, is *not a physical force*, as Newton had assumed. Gravity is a result of warped spacetime. Newton had got that wrong.

The man he'd imagined in free fall would feel weightless because he *was* weightless. Gravity was acting on the space and time around him rather than on *him*. Gravity wasn't a force between objects, but the shape of spacetime changing.

Today spacetime remains, with modifications, a central plank of particle physics and cosmology, and general relativity is a cornerstone.

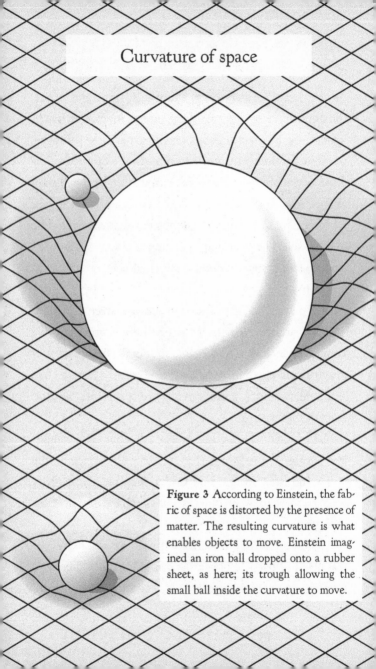

# Curvature of space

**Figure 3** According to Einstein, the fabric of space is distorted by the presence of matter. The resulting curvature is what enables objects to move. Einstein imagined an iron ball dropped onto a rubber sheet, as here; its trough allowing the small ball inside the curvature to move.

**General relativity** addresses big things: the stars and the universe.

**Quantum theory** addresses minutiae: atoms and smaller. It's a world of uncertainties, where everything is built on chance. And it's been called the most shocking discovery in the history of science. Einstein thought it catastrophic. 'God does not play dice,' he famously said, with a shake of his shaggy head. But he seems to have got that wrong.

Well, 'I'm no Einstein!' he once quipped.


# WONDERLAND

'Nobody understands quantum mechanics,' Nobel Prize-winning physicist Richard Feynman used to tell his pupils. So don't worry if you don't either. But that said, it isn't hard to absorb the basics, especially if, like Alice, you're prepared to make yourself very small – at least in expectations – and go along, open-mindedly, for the ride.

You're about to enter the unimaginably tiny subatomic world; a realm beyond all reason, where just about the only certainty is uncertainty. In this micro-world things can happen for no reason whatever. A bizarre reality, yet quantum theory correctly describes the universe at a subatomic level. It's everywhere, and it's you. So, fasten your seat belt, please, and let's get started.

The subatomic world, you will recall, is made up of quarks and electrons. **Quantum theory** or **quantum mechanics** (QM for short), describes how the subatomic world behaves. *Quantum* refers to the smallest indivisible chunk (quantity) of anything, and a *quantum leap* is the smallest possible change.

The first rule is that, unlike the everyday world, the quantum world is governed by *probability*. If you lay the table for a dinner party, you needn't fear it won't be there when your guests arrive. The quantum world has no such guarantees. You can only bet on the odds of something happening, or not. Predicting what is likely to happen is the best we can do.

At the theory's core is *wave-particle duality*. It turns out that subatomic objects, like photons and electrons, have two natures. They can behave like point particles (as Einstein said), but they can also behave like waves, as was previously thought. They have both properties.

We know this is so, because of patterns cast in a famous experiment using a two-slit screen (the Double

# Split screen experiment

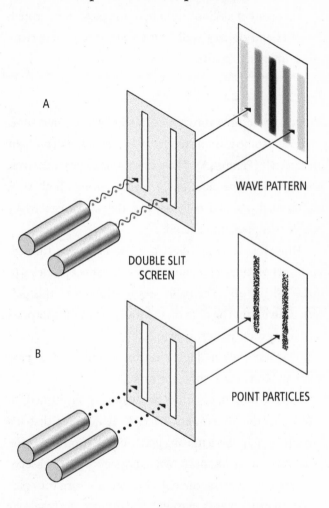

**Figure 4** This famous experiment of shooting particles through a double-slit screen revealed the weirdness of the subatomic world.

slit experiment). Shooting subatomic particles through the slits and on to a wall beyond produced some truly mind-boggling results.

Shooting electrons through both slits at the same time, produced some unexpected fuzzy bands of dark and light on the wall (Figure 4A). The pattern was typical of waves, not particles. The electrons, pouring through both slits, had fanned out and collided, like the waves caused by pebbles dropped into a pond.

However, shooting electrons *one at a time* through both slits produced the dots that you'd expect particles to make (Figure 4B). The really strange thing was, this pattern didn't last. The dots on the wall eventually morphed into fuzzy wave patterns, as in A.

That's not all. A single electron seemed able to pass through both slits at the same time.

This crazy, fluctuating behaviour is enshrined in physics as the *Uncertainty Principle*. It declares that it's impossible to know a moving particle's location and at the same time gauge its speed. When physicists try to observe or measure waviness, the objects instantly turn into particles. In other words, *our attention disturbs the behaviour of quantum matter*.

'What if a mouse looks at it?' a dubious Einstein declared.

But it's true.

Now this sounds daft, like so much else, but since a quantum particle's state can't be known, it's said to have a *superposition*, i.e. to be in all possible states *simultaneously* – as long as we don't look. But when we do, it's always a particle!

Superposition has been compared to a spinning coin. While it's spinning, the coin is both heads *and* tails. When it stops, it's one or the other. But here's the kicker. At a subatomic, quantum level the settled coin would remain both heads and tails – *until you looked at it.*

Schrodinger's cat is another classic example of super-position and probability blown up to visible, macro-world size. Here's a playful version.

The physicist Schrodinger's cat is shut in a box. The cat is in a *superposition*: it's in all possible states. Schrodinger suddenly remembers that experimental poison may have been left in the box. Is the poor creature dead or alive? Schrodinger will only know if he looks. Schrodinger opens the box, and the cat is dead. Did Schrodinger's curiosity kill the cat? Probably.

Even though quantum mechanics isn't understood, it works. And quantum and relativity theories work well together. Computers, lasers and nuclear reactors are examples of this.

But particle physics has failed in one crucially important aspect. It's been unable to include gravity in a QM 'theory of everything', which physicists aspire to.

Some hotly debated theories have sprouted to fill the gap.

**Quantum field theory** is accepted because it works. It claims the universe is made of particles and *fields*. But what exactly is a field?

Well, if someone is working in a field, it doesn't necessarily mean he's hoeing cotton. It could mean he's an historian or a scientist. That kind of field is an abstraction. The electromagnetic field, which carries electricity and light, was the first 'field' discovered in space, and it is physical. The level of reality of quantum fields is debatable. Some say quantum fields are a condition of space. Others claim that they *are* space. Space has a grainy structure, and particles are *vibrations* in it. In other words, fields and particles are the same thing, and the universe is one big quantum field of interactions. Reality isn't *things*; it's *interactions*. All is flux. There is no terra firma.

The recently confirmed Higgs field, containing the celebrated **Higgs boson particle**, gave quantum field theory a big boost. It's now accepted that all particles in the universe get mass from *interacting with Higgs particles in a Higgs field*. This is a big deal.

**String theory**, a variation of quantum field theory, posits the existence of infinitesimal strings of energy, smaller than quarks and shaped like ringlets, that can break open. The strings vibrate, rather like violin strings, with distinctive vibrations from the different particles. When they interact, the result is something like a musical universe playing its own highly peculiar symphony.

It sounds good, but string theory also claims that instead of Einstein's four spacetime dimensions, there are ten. The extra six are snugly curled up out of reach.

String theory and its competitors (below) depend on the existence of the so far undiscovered *graviton* particle.

**M-theory** combines string theory, relativity and quantum mechanics into the longed-for 'theory of everything'. It claims not 10 but 11 dimensions collectively called *branes*. But it isn't provable.

**Loop theory** is a *quantum theory of gravity*. Remember, gravity, according to Einstein, isn't a true force but a property of spacetime. So, it can be chopped into tiny chunks. This means that instead of a smooth fabric, spacetime is like a roughly woven cloth of intersecting, energy-exchanging quantum loops.

## BEYOND THE FRINGE

Before we end our meander along the shores of Wonderland, let's glance at a handful of ultra-strange goings-on that relativity and quantum physics have thrown up. Although a long way from being understood, some are already being successfully used by science and industry.

**Quantum entanglement**, or 'spooky action', to use Einstein's phrase, refers to the absolutely mind-boggling ability of a separated pair of particles to communicate *instantly* with each other, even from opposite sides of the galaxy. Any change to the state of one particle automatically affects the other – and faster than the speed of light. Experiments with particle pairs over much shorter distances have shown this extraordinary situation to be true. And no pre-programming occurred.

This weird phenomenon has already spawned the development of quantum computers and unhackable cyber codes. A quantum internet is being explored. Quantum entanglement is more than just big news: it goes to the very core of quantum physics. A far-flung network of entangled particles could be the true fabric of the universe.

**Quantum tunnelling** Particles like electrons and protons can penetrate solid barriers. Somehow, they manage to tunnel through. It's thought they could be travelling through *micro-wormholes* – innumerable shortcuts through the universe that make spacetime resemble a sort of celestial Swiss cheese.

A super-duper quantum computer is on the way that uses both tunnelling and entanglement, with phenomenal results. (See page 168.)

**Quantum teleportation** involves using entangled particles to transport 'parcels' instantly from one place to another. They aren't copied. They are extinguished and recreated at their destinations. The original ceases to exist.

For now, only information translated into code is possible. But eventually entire quantum systems may be transported. Theoretically, people could be too. But given the zillions of atoms involved, it would be like moving Mount Everest in spoonfuls. And would your replacement really be you?

**MWI** or **Multiworlds Interpretation** is probably the most bizarre item on offer in the whole quantum bazaar. It declares that the quantum world is continually splitting into alternative versions of what is actually happening. With every action you make, your 'now universe' produces alternative universes where every possible outcome of that action is realised, including all that could have happened, but didn't. Unlike other parallel universe theories, Multiworld universes are *within this universe*, and could be very close by. But you will never know it.

If your macro-world common sense is shouting, 'Nonsense!' You're right, it literally is nonsensical. But MWI theory is favoured by many leading particle- and astro-physicists.

To be continued, presumably.

## To summarise:

- Time and motion are relative.

- Time and space are intertwined to create 'spacetime'.

- Physical objects warp the fabric of spacetime. The distortion enables objects to move through space.

- Gravity is a result of distorted spacetime.

- Quantum mechanics (QM) describes the behaviour of the subatomic world: a realm of uncertainty ruled by probability.

- Subatomic particles can perform amazing particle tricks. They can be point-like particles or behave as waves. But when observed they instantly become particles. Our attention affects their behaviour.

- A separated pair of particles can communicate instantly over vast distances.

- Your entire history, past and future, plus all possible alternatives of every action, could be taking place in different universes, as you read this.

- The universe appears to be a dynamic network of interconnected patterns of energy, 'quantum sands' which your every move affects. The so-called real world is an offspring.

# 5

# GETTING REAL

'*To be or not to be, that is the question.*'

Shakespeare, *Hamlet*

Hamlet is thinking of throwing in the towel. He's a depressed adolescent with family problems. He has no idea what this 'mortal coil' he thinks of shuffling off really is, but he's worried about what, if anything, might happen to him without it. Is there another reality, and would he fit in? He has a choice, and preferring the devil he knows, his stepfather, he decides to hang in there, for now.

Even though Hamlet isn't a real person, he sparks a keen sense of reality in our minds, one brought to life even more vividly when an actor fleshes out his Hamletness.

Shakespeare's profound understanding of human nature, and his wonder and curiosity about the heavens, permeate his plays. Through Hamlet he is pondering the ultimate question: life and death; what does it really mean?

Some 400 years later the head scratching continues. We now know that matter is made of atoms, but we still don't know how some of it came to be 'alive'. What precisely life is remains a subject for debate.

The scientific community has agreed that life is a condition peculiar to ourselves, animals and plants, insects, fungi and bacteria. A handful of specific definitions has emerged. In each case the candidate must possess *all* the listed factors in order to qualify. Those endowed with only a few, fail to make it into life.

Acceptable qualifications are: the ability to grow, reproduce, respond to stimuli and changes in environment, keep a stable metabolism and be vulnerable to evolution.

A shorter version requires the capacity to move, the possession of DNA, and being carbon-based.

A NASA definition is quite simply 'a self-sustaining system capable of Darwinian evolution.'

Early cultures and many Eastern religions have awarded life status to stones and statues. These, together with plants and animals, are believed to harbour a soul. Often, the soul can move from one entity to another, up or down the evolutionary chain, depending on its owner's previous behaviour.

In most Western religions a soul endows its owner with life and, in addition, guarantees a heavenly or hellish immortality, depending on how its owner has behaved. Plants, animals and insects, stones and statues are not eligible for this particular immortality club.

The soul is a fascinating and immensely appealing idea, a deep solace for death and a strong motive for ethical living. But like the graviton, although heavily counted on, there is so far no scientific evidence of its existence.

So, according to current scientific thinking, a tree is alive, a stone is not and probably never was, unless of course it's a fossil. While viruses hover transgender-like on a red line, their credentials under repeated review.


## START UPS

Even more uncertain than a definition of life is a bona fide description of its origins. There's little solid evidence to go on. The current belief is that life evolved from a single primitive ancestor between 4.5 and 3.8 billion years ago. It resulted from chance chemical combinations or else from particles or spores arriving from outer space via meteors. Nobody really knows.

It's thought that the earliest micro-organisms probably existed in alkaline hot springs (hydrothermal vents) on the ocean floor. Or if sunlight was a necessary factor, then in warm volcanic lakes. Or if water was a problem, then a warm lake shore.

They probably replicated by splitting in two.

The oldest known fossils, found in Western Australia, are 3.5 billion years old. Most represent colonies of *cyanobacteria*, a microbe indispensable to all life, and of which more later.

Traces of other microbe types show life was already branching out. Over the next billion years these archaic creatures slowly evolved into two single-celled groups: **bacteria** and **archaea**. Little more than tiny bags holding a few chemicals, the bag or *membrane* did the trick. By keeping chemicals together, they could interact, grow and divide, and did.

Bacteria are the oldest, most diverse, numerous and arguably therefore most successful organisms on the planet. Crucially, they provided the raw material for other life forms. Not only are we more or less their offspring, but they remain a significant part of us today – or we of them – as will be seen in Chapter 7.

Whether you've read or hopscotched to this point, you've reached the third incident in the trinity of extraordinary events that, together with atoms and the mysterious awakening of life, enabled the creation and diversity of all living creatures on the planet. The evolution of the **eukaryote cell** – *a cell with a nucleus containing genetic material.*

Exactly how the nucleus emerged is, like so much else, uncertain. But it's believed that about two billion years ago a bacterium got inside the body of its single-celled cousin, an *archaeon,* (mentioned above). This partnership sparked the development of *organelles,* tiny compartments or sub-organs inside cells that, over centuries of chemical reactions, led to multicellular life. Mosses, fungi, algae, dinosaurs, mosquitoes, butterflies, bees, trees, whales, frogs, birds, kangaroos, horses, chimpanzees, and of course ourselves – all living things – are the result. The same basic cells compose us all.

So, just as atoms are the building blocks of matter, *cells are the building blocks of life.* In these minute bags all life begins and is controlled throughout every living thing's lifetime.

# EMPIRE

Your body can be compared to a federation of tiny Lilliput-like states: its cells, where robotic workers slave away non-stop till they drop dead. All these micro-states are dedicated to the peace and well-being of that dynamic empire which you head. And it is truly vast. Your cells outnumber the earth's human population by some 10,000 times.

As overall ruler you have a few responsibilities: workers must be fed and sheltered and the empire's borders secured. Otherwise you are free to do pretty much as you please – go where you like and do what you want to do, basking in the knowledge that your reign is ordained by natural law, conceivably even God-given. So long as you avoid harmful collisions – with other empires, for instance – life should be hunky-dory.

Such powers would be dizzy-making, were they not taken for granted, as so often happens with inherited fiefs, which this one mostly is. But how well do you in fact know your imperial fief, its seething ever-changing populations; how they live and what they actually do? How powerful is the rule that you enjoy within it? After all, even a small revolt can be infectious.

Let's take a short trot around your domain.

# Eukaryote cell

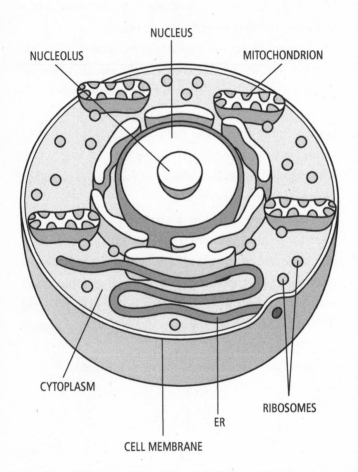

**Figure 5** Cross section of a cell with a nucleus. Called a *eukaryote* cell, its existence made the diversity of life possible.

# GEOGRAPHY

The trillions of cells in your body comprise some 200 types. Genetically identical, their *shape* defines their job. The largest cell has the diameter of a human hair, but most are 1/10 that size. It's simply inconceivable.

Inside each cell's bag-like **membrane** are two main areas: *cytoplasm* and *organelles* (sub-organs).

**Cytoplasm** is the treacle-like water that *organelles* are moored in. Each cell is about 70% water. (When you reflect that your atoms are 99.9% empty space and your cells 70% water, your imperial gravitas may feel somewhat punctured.)

The surrounding *membrane* gives each cell double-layered protection. The outer layer has sticky proteins, used for gluing the cell to others. (Organelles have membranes too, but simpler.)

Far and away the most important organelle is the **nucleus**. It contains the *genome* (DNA), which calls the shots: growth, cell renewal, body functions, and sometimes death (all of which more later). DNA rightly shows its family likeness to bacteria.

**Mitochondria**, sausage-shaped organelles, are the cell's power plants. All cell energy is made here. A cell has several mitochondria, and some cells have hundreds. Mitochondria also contain a bit of DNA.

**Ribosomes** are amazing micro-factories where cell proteins are made. Some cells have millions of ribosomes.

**ER** (*endoplasmic reticulum*) Here, newly-made proteins are folded into the right shape for their jobs and transported to the right locations.

**Lysosomes** help digest food and dispose of waste. If starved they will readily gobble up nearby organelles.

**Cytoskeleton**, a filament network, gives the cell flexibility while keeping organelles inside.

## BODY BUILDING

All cells are mainly composed of four elements: *hydrogen, oxygen, carbon* and *nitrogen*. Joined in different ways, the four elements make four sorts of molecules: *proteins, carbohydrates* (sugars), *nucleic acids* and *lipids* (fatty acids).

And that's it! Without this teamwork cells could not be made and life would not exist.

# HOW IT WORKS

**Proteins** are the workers, and they work hard. They build the cell, make new molecules, help fight infections, break down food for digestion and regulate body tissues and organs. Most human diseases are said to result from protein malfunction.

Proteins are *chains* of **amino acids**. The *sequence* of amino acids in the chain determines the protein. The sequenced chain is folded into the 3D shape that keys the protein to its particular job. Your body has thousands of different proteins that do different jobs. Yet all are made from 20 amino acids arranged in different sequences.

*Enzymes* are specialised proteins of immense importance. They are catalysts: they speed up chemical reactions, sometimes as much as a million times. *Every chemical reaction has its own enzyme. Lactase,* for example, breaks down *lactose* (a sugar) in milk, so it's digestible. All children have the enzyme, but not all adults. Common in people with a herding ancestry, most others lose the enzyme as they grow up, so can't digest milk.

**Nucleic acids**, molecules inside the cell nucleus, run the whole show. They store and transfer genetic information. There are two kinds: **DNA** (*deoxyribonucleic acid*) and its cousin, **RNA** (*ribonucleic acid*). What these two accomplish is unparalleled in life and evolution, as will be seen in Chapter 8.

## To summarise:

- Life is a self-sustaining condition. Its key features are common to all living things, but its origin is something of a mystery.

- The diversity of plant and animal life became possible when a cell developed a nucleus containing DNA.

- Life, at its simplest, involves four main elements that make four different molecules, of which proteins and the nucleic acids DNA and RNA, have crucial importance.

- Proteins are made from 20 different amino acids folded into special 3D shapes, following DNA's instructions.

- Proteins build cells and cells build bodies.

# 6

# BUSY BODIES

*'Those little grey cells. It is up to them.'*
Agatha Christie

Agatha Christie was focused on brain cells, but her pithy observation applies to all of them. Your cells are multi-taskers *par excellence*. They turn food into body molecules and energy. They twitch and contract so that you can move. They also keep a tidy house, make protective antibodies and attack invaders. But their biggest job of all is self-replication. It's by cells multiplying themselves that your body grows and stays in good repair.

You're made from a single layer of cells that, following DNA instructions, divided into three layers. The outermost layer formed your skin and nervous system. The middle layer made muscles, skeleton, heart, blood, kidneys; the inner layer, your gut, liver and lungs.

While like-minded cells teamed up to make your *tissues* and *organs*, some cells, mainly blood cells and stem cells, kept their independence.

**Red blood cells'** main job is carrying inhaled oxygen to your body tissues and *carbon dioxide* back to your lungs, to be exhaled. As you read this sentence two million red blood cells were made in your body. That's 150 billion new blood cells per hour. Exhausting just to think about.

**Stem cells** are invaluable back-pocket plans. Each one is a *tabula rasa*, free to take on the identity of a tissue cell needing repair. The largest supply exists in embryos and the placenta. These are 100% adaptable and can become almost any type of cell, in anybody's body. They are never rejected.

Most adult tissues contain a small supply of stem cells, but only some of them – those in bone marrow, for example – can be used in other parts of the body. Recently, however, scientists turned ordinary mouse cells back into their embryonic state, as multi-purpose stem cells. The breakthrough promises a brilliant future for adult human stem cells.

**White blood cells**, notably B-cells and T-cells, form your immune system. They kill foreigners: viruses, parasites and harmful bacteria, and make antibodies. Some can remember previous invaders, and attack them. But if they mistake a friend for foe and, say, attack your body's cells, an auto-immune disease like diabetes or arthritis can result. Equally, an organ transplant will be rejected by them.

**Nerve cells** are your body's sensory message service. They pass information between sense organs and your brain via electrical impulses. Nerve cells make muscles move, horns sound, food taste and mosquito bites itch. They are described in greater detail later on.

**Talk talk.** In addition to a sensory telegraph system, cells talk to each other. Using chemical signals – hormones and neurotransmitters – they send out millions of signals every day. Scientists working to crack their codes have had a degree of success: prescribed pills will often hack into cell chat to make something happen, or not.

# GET UP AND GO
Cells need food for growth, energy and repairs. Here's how it works.

When you eat, your digestive system breaks food proteins down into their original amino acids. These are carried round by the blood and re-assembled as the material your body needs.

Food and oxygen are necessary to make **cell energy**. Cell energy is made in the cell's *mitochondria* (see page 47). It's converted from food energy and stored in feisty little molecules called **ATP** (*adenosine triphosphate*).

*ATP* provides energy for every living thing on earth. In a series of knock-on chemical reactions, it stores, releases and delivers energy to needy spots in the cell. This ancient, unusually convoluted process is the same for an amoeba as it is for us.

You have around a thousand million ATP molecules per cell. They are replaced every two minutes. It's a very busy business.

## BEING AND NON-BEING

A cell's life sentence of unrelenting, repetitive slave labour, is the same in all living things. But cell lifespans vary enormously. So do their rates of replacement. You lose some 90 million cells a minute, but 90 million new ones are created at the same time. Red blood cells live about four months, white blood cells for about a year.

Colon cells last four days and sperm cells, three. (But 1500 a second can be produced, on demand.) Brain cells are the exception. They rarely replicate. The ones you have right now are with you more or less for life.

Surprisingly, cells contain their own death warrants. Issued with impunity, a cell is usually healthy when it dies. It commits suicide for your greater good: to keep cell balance and counter injuries and infections. DNA gives the command and special enzymes go to work. They chop the condemned cell up or they engulf it.

**Replication**. Cells originate from other cells, going back to single-celled Eve. They have two kinds of replication: *mitosis* and *meiosis*. Each has a different goal.

**Mitosis** services the body. It makes new cells to repair tissues, keeps life ticking over and your body generally shipshape.

Directed by the nucleus, the cell grows in size, doubling all its parts. The duplicate material separates itself by going to the opposite end of the cell. The cell membrane contracts in the middle, and the cell splits into identical twin cells (identical also to the sacrificed parent). In short, all cells are clones.

The instructions needed to bring this off are claimed to rival building a supercomputer.

**Meiosis** produces brand new beings. Though similar to mitosis, it involves not one but *two* cell divisions. The cell's 23 chromosome pairs are halved and four sperm or egg cells (depending on the donor) are produced.

At fertilisation, a sperm and egg cell, each containing half their chromosome pairs, combine to make a new cell, called a *zygote*. The 23 chromosome *pairs* (half from each parent) have been restored.

The zygote divides and begins to multiply. Nine months later a unique individual is born. (See also Chapter 8.)

Special *hox genes* control what goes where. You have 39. A mistake could add a finger or misplace an arm. (Anne Boleyn was said to have had an extra finger on one hand.)

Humans are made from some 200 different types of cells. We know roughly how the assembly happens, but we don't know *why*. Most probably it's happenstance. Possibly it's obscurely ordained. Conceivably it's one bodily empire hedging its survival bets by merger with a neighbouring one. Or it's a combination; or something else. But whatever the motivation, this complex and astonishing process has fuelled an ongoing mixing of genes that, with natural selection's help, has produced the roughly 10 million different types of organisms alive on the earth today.

## REALITY CHECK

Nature is a brilliant designer. She works by trial and error, and she favours organisation and division of labour. Four billion years of natural selection has produced an interdependent world of growing complexity.

From *one cell* has come not only microbes, fungi, insects, plants, and animals, but a number of looser organisations: beehives, anthills, shoals, herds, prides, families, tribes – bodies wired together by ingrained social instincts as well as strong genetic connections.

Stealing nature's blueprint, we've invented similar bodies of our own: teams, clubs, corporations, nations, empires. All follow nature's pattern book. They are born, have specific functions, play by a rule book, cooperate, replace their weak spots, sacrifice for the greater good, and eventually fall to pieces.

Despite your own strong sense of being a *person*, the average overall lifespan of your cells is 7 to 10 years. Few molecules in your body today were present in childhood. And yet, despite several bodily remakes, you still feel that you are you. But are you? Have your replaced cells, being clones, made you the same person, assuming all went well? The best referee is, of course, your brain. Your brain cells have been with you from the beginning. They are best-suited to tell you who you are. And only rarely do they make mistakes, and say for instance that you are Napoleon. But the fact it can happen proves they are not infallible.

No body can make new cells indefinitely; a total breakdown is inevitable. When it occurs, every body will rejoin the general melting pot, for recycling. But here's a rub: your atoms will continue to live forever. In fact, their recycling has already begun. An atom you shed yesterday on the street could before long sustain a pizza or a pope. It might, in time, settle inside a spaceship or its astronaut, and spend eons on another planet, before moving on. *This is a science-certified form of immortality* – for what it's worth. It's also a reminder that everything is essentially the same.

## To summarise:

- Cells build all living things.

- Digestion breaks food down and, combined with oxygen, produces proteins needed for cell repair.

- The ATP molecule is the source of cell energy for all living things.

- Cell replication has two forms. *Mitosis* enables body growth and cell repair. *Meiosis* produces a new being.

- Cells will commit suicide to protect their host.

- Living things die but their atoms are immortal.

# 7

# FELLOW TRAVELLERS

*'The most outstanding feature of life's history is a constant domination by bacteria.'*

Stephen Jay Gould

Microbes are the oldest and most prolific living things on earth, and arguably they are the most successful. Invisible to the eye, the first microbes emerged at least 3.5 billion years ago, probably from hot springs in the oceans or possibly via meteorites that crashed into the planet. They comprise 99% of all living things.

*Bacteria, viruses, archaea* and *fungi* are the main types. But bacteria and viruses affect us most. They are everywhere (including cropping up repeatedly in this book). It's said there are as many bacteria in a gram of soil, and viruses in a cup of seawater, as people on the planet.

Recently, vast numbers of bacteria have been discovered living deep underground. Even three miles down, they eke out a lethargic slow-motion existence between rock crevices, nibbling on rocky crumbles for energy. Some scientists are beginning to wonder if life could have started underground.

Remember, a bacterium probably gave us life. Teaming up with its archaeon cousin, it produced the first cell with a nucleus (page 44). Both our genes and mitochondria (energy powerhouses) show signs of bacterial origins.

What's more, if you think your body belongs exclusively to you, you are mistaken. The truth is it's a highly popular, full board, microbial hotel. Some 10,000 microbe species reside there. But bacteria and viruses are the main residents. Most of them earn their keep by doing useful work, and many are downright indispensable. But infection and disease are part of the package too.

# BACTERIA

A *bacterium* is a minute, independent cell containing a bit of DNA, plus some ribosomes (protein building factories). Identified mainly by its shape, the most notable types are spheres (*cocci*), rods (*bacilli*) and spirals (*spirilla*). Some bacteria have hairs to better attach themselves to other cells; others have propeller-like tails for scooting about. A number even possess a compass (magnetic crystals that point them north).

Most bacteria get energy by eating organic waste. But a few use photosynthesis, and some of them can use both methods.

Bacteria excel at self-replication. Mostly, they do it by splitting in two. The gut bacterium, *E. coli*, is a good example. It can divide every 20 minutes. This means that in 12 hours 1 bacterium can make 70 billion copies of itself.

## Them and us

Most bacteria live *around* your cells, not in them. They cover your skin and line the inside of your mouth. But their favourite residence is of course your gut. Here, as part of a large and bustling kitchen, they help prepare your meals, breaking food down into digestible sugars, and freely helping themselves to leftovers. They also make vitamins K and B12, and deal with dangerous poisons. In addition, we now know they can seriously affect your mental state.

Recently, it's been discovered that, like the brain, gut bacteria produce neurotransmitters, e.g. *dopamine* and *serotonin*, that govern our moods. Special gut cells send out pulse-like signals to the brain, via the *vagus nerve*, which connects gut and brain. It's now thought Parkinson's disease, long associated with dopamine production, may start in the gut and not the brain, as was previously thought.

What's more, when gut bacteria from depressed humans were implanted in microbe-free mouse guts, the mice showed clear signs of depression.

Although a blood–brain barrier exists to keep foreigners from paddling freely around in your bloodstream, enzymes from the gut bacteria *gingivalis* (which causes gum disease) recently turned up in Alzheimer patients' brains. It may play a part in triggering the disease.

Much of the above is news, and how it works isn't understood. But it's increasingly clear that the microbes in your *microbiome,* your total microbe population, are as important to your survival and personality as is your brain.

## The bad guys

Of course, bacteria infamously cause diseases. Medieval plagues like the Black Death were bacteria based. So are TB, typhoid, strep throat, anthrax, Lyme's disease, syphilis, cholera, dysentery and diarrhoea – to name only a few.

Normally, your immune system takes care of infectious diseases. But microbes help too. Many of them have chemical brews able to kill other microbes. This was first noticed by scientist Alexander Fleming, when a green fungus (mould) killed the bacteria in one of his petri dishes. It was a eureka moment. Putting the killer fungus to use, Fleming developed the first antibiotic, *penicillin*. Today, fungi and bacteria form the base of nearly every antibiotic in our medical war chest.

**Antibiotics** either kill bacteria or impede their spread by chemically blocking their growth or replication. (Penicillin prevents bacteria from making cell walls.) The downside is that antibiotics mostly kill indiscriminately. In other words, taking the bad guys out takes out some of the good guys too.

*Probiotics* are bacteria you can eat to improve a troubled gut. Faecal transplants, used for more serious gut infections, are even more successful.

But as the world is finding out, bacteria's high-speed replication and mutation rates mean that new, resistant strains quickly replenish the decimated ranks. It's a war we're in danger of losing. Some estimates suggest that by 2050 more people will die of drug-resistant bacteria than of cancers. The search for new antibiotics is urgent. It could be the slow-poke microbes living underground will come to our rescue, for a time.

## Multi-taskers

Bacteria also cater to out-of-body interests. Their enzymes wash your clothes and ferment your food and drink (cheese, beer, wine, yogurt). They can treat sewage, remove oil seepages and help to fertilise soil. Biotech (combined biology and technology) is opening the door to all sorts of novel uses of bacteria, as will be seen in Chapter 13.

# VIRUSES

In contrast to the myriad bacteria living in extreme conditions underground, a vast stream of viruses (and bacteria) circles the globe above the climate system. Possibly swept there by the winds, some 800 million viruses are said to descend daily on to every square metre of the earth.

Viruses are the most abundant entities on earth. Simpler and much smaller than bacteria, a virus consists of a protein capsule containing RNA or DNA, but never both. Some have a fatty outer envelope for extra protection.

However, it's debatable whether or not they are alive! Therefore, whether they qualify as microbes. Viruses don't eat or grow. They even lack the tackle to reproduce. And yet, ironically, when it comes to speedy replication, these sub-lives take the cake.

Although unable to replicate themselves, they carry around a genetic blueprint for its accomplishment. Their plan is to trick other creatures' cells into doing the job for them. In other words, viruses are parasites. They hijack living cells and reproduce by infecting them. That's all they do.

Replicate. Replicate. Replicate. The result permeates all life and the effects can sometimes be horrific, as we've recently been finding out.

## How it works

Of the millions of virus species that exist, humans attract a mere 250 or so. Each virus type favours a particular kind of cell. Cold and flu viruses attack air passages and respiratory tracts; hepatitis prefers the liver. A virus's shape and surface is its key to penetrating a suitable cell. One virus can capture a whole cell and order it to make thousands of virus selfies.

A virus never enters the victim's cell. It sticks itself on to the cell's exterior and injects its DNA or RNA. The bamboozled cell goes obediently to work and, following its new orders, makes a copy of the virus – repeatedly.

Soon the enslaved cell is full of viruses. Bursting out (usually killing the host cell en route) a viral nano-army marches forth to impose its blind robotic will upon the neighbouring cells. As the army grows with each conquest, so does the threat to nearby organs and tissues. Sometimes the affected creature dies.

**Retroviruses** carry RNA not DNA. But DNA is needed to make the protein a virus needs in order to replicate. Using a special enzyme, they turn their RNA into DNA, before attacking their victims. (If a sperm or egg is infected, the virus can get passed on.) The common cold and most flu viruses with spiky exteriors are called coronaviruses. Also HIV, Sars and world-shaking Covid-19.

Sometimes a virus's DNA stays dormant in the host cell, dividing whenever the host cell does. This can drip feed an infection that goes on for years. It can also weaken a host's natural immunity. Tumours occur when viral-infected cells go berserk and cell replication is non-stop.

An unchecked virus can spark a pandemic the equal of a nuclear bomb. The Covid-19 virus reached every country on earth in only three months.

## Fighting back

Viruses are fought in three ways: by immune systems, vaccinations and anti-viral drugs.

Special white blood 'memory cells' can recognise a virus that's caused previous harm. If it returns, they can kill it before it spreads.

*Vaccines* exploit this remarkable ability. A bit of the infectious virus, say measles, small enough for an immune system to manage, is injected into a child. If a measles virus turns up later on, it's recognised and war is instantly declared.

Antiviral drugs work by interfering chemically to prevent virus replication.

Some viral diseases, like smallpox, have been eradicated in humans by widespread live vaccination. Others, such as polio, yellow fever, chicken pox and measles, are *prevented* by vaccinations. Still others, AIDS for instance, can only be held in check. The common cold continues unabated.

## Good guys

Not all viruses are bad news. **Bacteriophages – phages** for short – are viruses that attack *bacteria*; most especially, gut bacteria. In doing so, they unwittingly protect their host. Your gut contains something like a million billion phages, whose bacteria-destroying abilities help to keep a microbial gut balance.

We now know viruses can pick up bits of the host's DNA, by mistake, and take it along from one cell to the next. This gave scientists a brilliant idea. If phages could carry bits of DNA around, why shouldn't they carry other stuff as well? The idea took root. Today, phages carry medicine to infected cells. And a plan to use them as nano-vans and storage bins is underway. At MIT, they are being converted into nano-batteries able to store renewable energy, with minimum toxic waste.

Phages may have been nature's first immune system. Despite being seriously dangerous, today they're proving useful in a variety of new and fascinating ways. A bio-technique of truly life-changing significance, using phages, will be seen in the next chapter.

## To summarise:

- Microbes are the most populous beings on the planet. They cause diseases but are also crucial to our existence. It's a love–hate relationship.

- *Bacteria* help digest food and remove waste. They fight diseases, and they cause them. They also affect moods.

- *Viruses* are parasites that hijack and reproduce inside other beings' cells.

- Bacteriophages (*aka* phages) are viruses that attack gut bacteria and help keep a microbial balance.

- Biotechnology is using phages for numerous new transport systems.

- Viruses and bacteria are super-speed replicators able to produce superbugs immune to extant drugs.

# Who Are You?

# 8

# THE SECRET AGENT

*'I think, therefore, I am.'*     René Descartes

With the above assertion, the seventeenth-century philosopher René Descartes ignited an Age of Reason, offering a succinct and reasoned proof of his existence. Everyone could relax; if they could think, they existed. It stood to reason.

Yet the sentence in its fullest expression surely means, 'I think, therefore, I think I am.' Quite another thing – and perhaps a greater truth.

Descartes was fixated on his soul and seems to have regarded his body as a rather tiresome hanger-on or mortal coil to be profitably shaken off. He declared himself to be 'a thinking soul'. He'd no idea that a physical organ (his brain) was doing the thinking, or that an organelle (the cell nucleus housing his genome) masterminded his debatable existence and had made him who he was.

# GENE SPEAK

Safely tucked away inside every cell's teeny tiny nucleus, the **genome** is life's most precious if ubiquitous treasure. This amazing store of hereditary information controls the growth, body functions, personal appearance and, most significant, reproduction, of all living things. Genes tell your cells what to do and when to do it. A ticket to life and custodian of its maintenance, genes were in the driver's seat long before the organ that became the human brain turned up. So, first things first:

**Genes** are normally packaged in sausage-like **chromosomes**. Human chromosomes come in pairs: one chromosome from each parent. You have 23 matched pairs, with one exception: chromosome 23, the sex chromosome. Females have a matched pair dubbed XX. But males have one X and one Y. It's been the making of them.

*Each chromosome contains a single molecule* of celebrated **DNA**. Twisted into the famous ladder-like spiral or double helix (see page 78), the ladder's 'rungs' contain the chemical code that makes **genes**. Each gene determines something about you. But numerous genes usually interact to produce a characteristic. You have some 22,000 genes in all.

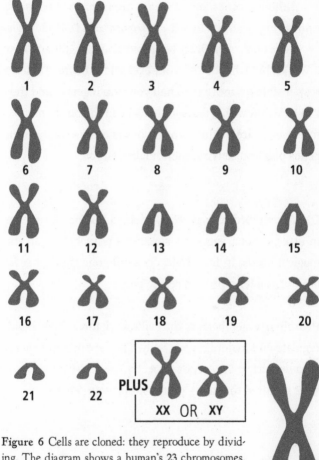

**Figure 6** Cells are cloned: they reproduce by dividing. The diagram shows a human's 23 chromosomes. Pinched in the centre, they are about to split and form two identical cells. The process is described in Chapter 6. The 23rd chromosome: XX and XY, female and male respectively, determines gender.

Although genes and DNA are often referred to as the same thing, a gene is in fact *one segment of a DNA molecule*.

Genes not only direct how your body is built and how it works, but what colour your eyes and skin are. They are responsible for more than half your intelligence, and they can land you with a disease that's been in your family before. Genes are behind your moods and personality. Your genes plus your environment make you *you*.

DNA's extraordinary powers, wielded behind the scenes in utter secrecy, suggest a sorcerer's notebook of arcane magical spells. In fact, DNA does only one thing: *it codes for proteins*. It's a protein recipe book.

**Proteins**, remember, are the cell's work force. They build, regulate and maintain your body. They are made of *chains of amino acids*. DNA codes specify the *sequence of amino acids* required to make a particular protein. That's it.

You have some 100,000 different proteins in your body and 20 amino acids make all of them. Briefly, it goes like this:

1.  A DNA molecule is unspooled from its tightly stuffed chromosome.

2.  An enzyme unzips the molecule down the middle, as shown in Figure 7 (p. 78), separating the two strands.

3.  DNA's single-stranded cousin, RNA, copies the *stretch of DNA* that contains the recipe for making the *amino acids* needed to make the desired protein.

4.  RNA then delivers the recipe to the cell's protein-making factory, a **ribosome**, moored in the cell's fluid.

5.  The coded recipe is translated, the protein built and sent to the right spot in the cell.

DNA never leaves the nucleus.

# DNA double helix

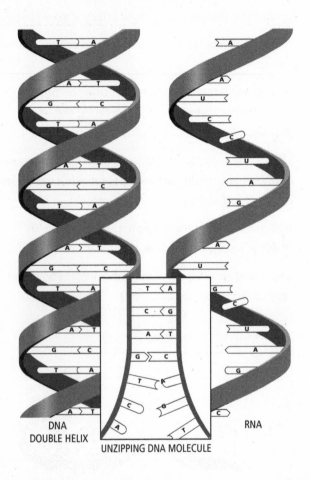

**DNA**
**DOUBLE HELIX**  **UNZIPPING DNA MOLECULE**  **RNA**

**Figure 7** The famous DNA molecule, in the shape of a double helix, contains life's blueprint. The inset shows the two strands being unzipped, prior to copying.

# THE RECIPE

- DNA codes are really simple. They only have 4 letters: ATCG. These stand for 4 *nucleic acids* called *bases*.

- A binds to T and C binds to G. So, each 'rung' in the ladder is either an A+T or C+G (see diagram).

- Each stretch of gene has a start and finish 'button'.

- The 4-letter alphabet, ATCG, makes 3-letter words (GGA, for instance).

- Each 3-letter word codes for 1 amino acid.

- A specific combination of amino acids codes for 1 protein.

- 64 combinations are possible.


To recap: the DNA molecule is a spiral ladder. Its 'rungs' comprise 4 chemical bases, ATCG. These 4 letters make the 3-letter words that code for the 20 amino acids needed to make all the proteins in your body. That's the recipe for life. Amazingly simple, isn't it?

# Leftovers

In addition to your nuclear-based genome, you have a bit of DNA called **mtDNA** squirrelled away inside another organelle, your *mitochondria*, the cell's power plant, described earlier (see page 47).

Mitochondria were probably independent microbes millions of years ago. The mtDNA chromosome is circular and free-floating, like bacteria's. It contains 37 genes.

mtDNA is exceptional in another respect. It's passed exclusively from mother to daughter. Men inherit it but can't pass it on. This means it doesn't get shuffled about in *meiosis*. It's been passed down relatively pure from your female ancestor, genetic Eve, some 300,000 years ago. mtDNA's comparatively few mutations make it useful in tracing ancestry. Each mutation marks a new bud on the evolutionary tree.

**RNA,** which records and delivers DNA messages, is a lot older than its more famous double-stranded cousin. Eons ago it may have been self-replicating. But DNA proved more efficient in the protein-making department, so eventually took over the factory.

# A closer look

The recipe for a single protein can be thousands of DNA letters long. Some proteins need an input from more than one gene. Haemoglobin, for instance, gets genes from chromosome 16 and also chromosome 11.

Chromosome 11 codes for hundreds of different genes. Haemoglobin occupies a 1600-letter stretch, of which 146 make proteins. Others address when, where and how much protein to make.

How all this works is largely a mystery. We only know 5% of the universe's composition. We know even less what all our genes are up to, if anything. The fact is, fewer than 2% of our genome actually codes for proteins; 98% of DNA's functions are unknown.

Dubbed **junk DNA**, some of this unknown stuff may indeed be useless, the remains of viral infections and lost causes. But some of it clearly plays a regulating role, turning genes off and on. We still have much to learn. But uselessly toting a lot of baggage around for thousands of generations is unnatural.

## Calling the shots

Genetic science is pioneer country, and it's here the biggest changes to human life, as we know it, will probably take place.

The human genome was decoded in 2003. We know the positions of our 22,000+ genes, plus what many of them do. But words without sentences don't say much. Breaking the gene speech code should eventually give us the whole story. And with it, as scientists have pointed out, come the godlike powers to improve body functions, beat disease and, if legally allowed, adjust our bodies and food supplies to fit the demands of a future high-tech world.

Darwinian evolution, addressed in Chapter 10, is snail-like compared to the growing speed of modern technology. The **gene editing** process, CRISPR-Cas9, is a breathtaking example, with earth-shaking possibilities. It allows a faulty gene to be snipped out of its genome and altered or replaced to fix the fault.

Repairing a faulty gene sequence works as follows. A virus is used for transport. Its DNA is removed and replaced by the needed DNA. The virus injects the new DNA into a bacterium, as is its habit. Guided by RNA, the bacterium finds the needy spot. A protein, Cas9, snips out the faulty bit, and the replacement is neatly inserted.

If the altered gene is in an egg or sperm cell, it will be inherited by succeeding generations.

Such interventions, with their potential for good, for ill and ultimately for the creation of Superperson, should keep moral opinions on the boil for many years.

# Tweaking

In the meantime, nature has her own ways of tweaking gene expression. In addition to **mutations**, there are **alleles** and the exciting new field of **epigenetics**.

Though cells have two copies of each gene (one from each parent), they aren't always precisely the same. When this happens they are called **alleles**.

You've probably heard of Mendel the monk, who crossbred garden peas. Some of his plants had white flowers, the others had purple flowers. When Mendel crossbred them, *all* the offspring were purple. But when he crossbred those, a ratio of 3 purple to 1 white-flowered plants showed up. Only when he bred only white flowers were all the offspring white.

Mendel had discovered that a gene pair can have different *strengths* of expression. In other words, some traits are *dominant* and others therefore weaker, or *recessive*. In Mendel's flowers, purple was dominant and white was recessive. But nobody paid any attention.

We now know that slight genetic variations give rise to slightly different proteins, which can affect a gene's expression. Eye colour genes, for instance, have one allele for brown and one for blue. Brown is dominant, but if both brown-eyed parents carry a recessive allele for blue, they have one chance in four of producing a blue-eyed baby. Brown hair is dominant, but two recessive alleles will produce a blond (as will your hairdresser).

Whether you fold your hands with your right or left thumb on top, or whether or not you can roll your tongue, are also allele governed. (If you can roll your tongue but neither of your parents can, then one or both of them are not your biological parents.) Alleles can also express disease. Cystic fibrosis lurks in a recessive allele/gene. If both parents carry the gene, their children have a one-in-four chance of inheriting the disease. It's caused by a single gene mutation.

**Mutations** result from genetic mistakes: a code letter is miscopied or a gene damaged. If the error is in an egg or sperm cell, then it can be passed on.

Useful mutations can be included in genomes; useless ones get weeded out. But if sort of useful, a gene could stay on as a recessive trait. Sickle cell anaemia is an example. It can kill you, but it guards against malaria while you live.

**Epigenetics** is something that's causing a lot of excitement – some would even say, a revolution – in biology. But it's early days.

Epigenetics involves factors *outside* genes that *alter gene expression*. Diet, age, lifestyle and disease can cause certain chemicals in cells to switch genes on and off. This affects which genes are expressed. Incredibly, in some cases the changes have turned up *in the next generation*. That is what's causing the fireworks.

Honeybees are a classic example of epigenetics in nature. Worker bees and their sister, who becomes queen, are genetically identical. They are clones. Yet the queen bee is much bigger, has no sting, makes eggs and lives a lot longer. Her worker bee sisters are small and infertile.

Diet makes the difference. The queen eats only royal jelly throughout her life. The soon-to-be-workers get only a few days on royal jelly, then look after themselves. They live on pollen and honey. It's recently been found that a plant chemical they ingest, alters their gene expression. Amazingly, this creates a separate caste. (How queens are selected is yet unknown.)

Epigenetic research has focused on a process called *methylation* (**Me** for short). This involves a particular molecule ($CH_3$) that can stick to DNA.

Some genes are naturally methylated. But $CH_3$ can coat normally *unmethylated* genes. This can shut them down or skew how they're read. Therefore, how they make proteins.

In a widely reported experiment, the normally methylated *agouti* gene in normally brown mice was demethylated (its coating of methyl removed). The mice got fat and turned yellow. More amazingly, their offspring were also born yellow and soon they too got fat.

Another study involved babies born in Holland's 1944–45 wartime famine. Born with reduced DNA methylation in a particular gene, the babies were susceptible to diabetes and cardiovascular disease. Unexpectedly, these tendencies have turned up in their children and grandchildren, *but not in any of their genomes*. The effects were epigenetic.

Passing *acquired* characteristics on to the next generation had been declared impossible. To do so without alterations to the genome, if true, is truly sensational. It could transform modern genetics – also morals, if the effects of our behaviour could in some cases be passed on to our children.

**End game** In addition to ceaseless cell activity, tiny 'hourglasses' inside cells keep time. These are **telomeres**. They don't look like hourglasses, but like shoelace tips. One is attached to each end of every chromosome. Every time cells divide, their telomeres get shorter, and shorter, and shorter, until eventually they're gone. The cells stop dividing, and time is up.

Telomere length is gene related. It offers a longer life to some, but not to others. (An enzyme, *telomerase*, can rebuild telomeres – but it's usually turned off before birth.)

**New life** In a landmark achievement, a synthetic, *computer-designed genome* has recently been created and implanted in *E. coli* bacteria. The bacteria's cells followed the artificial DNA's instructions. They even replicated, albeit very slowly.

Arguably, a new life form has been created.

## To summarise:

- DNA masterminds life. Its 4-letter alphabet makes 3-letter words that instruct amino acids to make the proteins that build bodies.

- Alleles, small gene variations, express dominant and recessive traits.

- Gene mutations can happen when a gene is miscopied, damaged or changed by disease. If egg or sperm cells are involved, the mutation can be passed on.

- Genes can be physically edited to correct mistakes and prevent genetically caused diseases.

- Genes altered by the environment have turned up in the next generation, without altering the genetic code.

- A computer-generated, synthetic bacteria genome has been created.

# 9

# THE THINKING TALKING HEAD

*'I feel, therefore, I exist.'*     Thomas Jefferson

Writing to fellow former president, John Adams, Thomas Jefferson thus contested Descartes' famous declaration: 'I think, therefore, I am'. Although a disciple of the Age of Reason, Jefferson had twigged that reason was only half the plot – the reliable, self-governing half. Feelings were of great importance too. Without them you wouldn't know you were alive.

But feelings could be troublesome. A wise and careful balance must be struck. Jefferson even wrote a short 'Dialogue Between My Head and My Heart', examining the end of his affair with a charming and talented, but married, Englishwoman. His head had narrowly prevailed.

We too think like Jefferson. When a problem arises, we review the evidence rationally, make a considered decision and, if necessary, deputise our willpower to impose it. It's the best formula we have, but it is seriously flawed. It isn't how brains work.

The human brain is the most complex object on the planet, so far. A vast communication system of multiple, interacting networks, it governs movement and vital functions, processes thoughts and feelings, stores memories and invents emotions. It bestows the power of speech and, with the aid of our five senses, interprets the outside world.

In doing so it creates a sense of the world we call **reality**, a feeling of personal being within it that we call **self**, and a self-reflective awareness we call our **consciousness**.

Brains are basically patternmaking freaks. The patterns are both hardwired (genetic) and laid down by experiences, mostly collected by the senses. All 'rational' decisions depend on previous input *plus* any related information the brain happens to release. And we've no conscious control over that.

Many decisions, however, need little or no rational input. When Roger Federer lands a tennis ball just inside the line and just outside his opponent's reach, it happens before he even knows he hit it. He acted spontaneously. A conscious decision would have slowed him down.

Processing sensory input takes time; autopilot is faster and more energy efficient.

Federer fans too see the play only when it's over. This means we live marginally in the past. Yet our conscious self takes credit for every decision when more often than not it's simply a bystander, a quasi-puppet operated by a stranger – our subconscious.

## HEAD START

Millions of years ago a primitive brain kept creatures breathing and their hearts beating. It enabled movement and enough awareness of the surroundings that, coupled with instincts for fight, freeze or flight, multiplied chances of survival.

A version of that brain is with us today, in the **brain stem** and **cerebellum** or 'little brain', of which more later. Add-ons, occurring over many centuries, filled our early ancestors' expanding skulls with new abilities and advantages. Mostly, they were crammed into a forebrain, the **cerebrum**. It's this bit we normally refer to as 'the brain'.

The whole package, your **central nervous system**, comprises *brain, spinal cord* and the *nerves* branching out from them, mostly to sense organs (Figure 8).

# Central nervous system

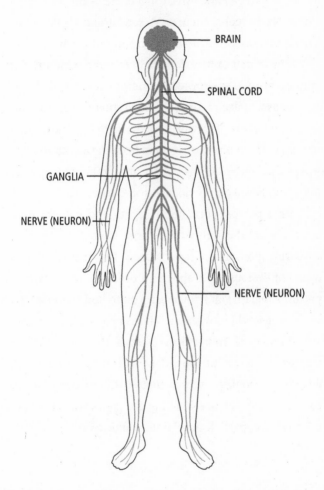

**Figure 8** The body's neuron messenger system is masterminded by the brain.

**Sense organs** – ears, eyes, tongue, etc. – collect impressions. **Nerve cells** (**neurons**) send them to the brain. There, they're sorted, acted upon and/or filed away.

Your stored impressions help to build a picture that connects you to and protects you from, the outside world. But the assembled picture, although convincing, is a sham; it's make-believe. The world has no sights, sounds, smells or tastes. The brain weaves them from the atoms and light waves that sense organs collect and brains organise and interpret, based on previously stored patterns.

For a person born blind, sights and colours don't exist. Should the ability to see arise later on in life, a bewildering gibberish of light is seen. This is because your eyes continuously flit about. In order to 'see' anything, patterns must be laid down early on to build a model that makes the world look stable. This is true of all five senses.

There is of course lots of stuff that we can't see: viruses, X-rays, neutrinos, dark matter and God knows what else, requiring senses that evolution saw no cause to encourage. Science is filling the gap, with telescopes, microscopes, particle accelerators and so on.

# Brain – four lobes

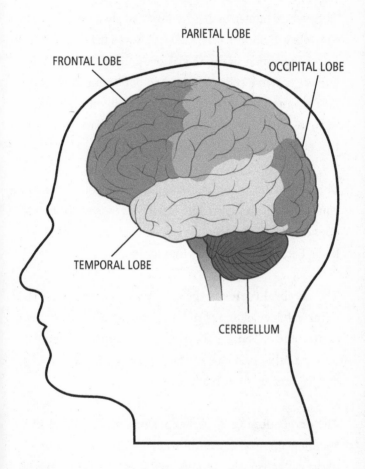

**Figure 9** Four lobes compose the cerebrum, which we normally call our 'brain'. Each lobe has specialised features. Below it, sits an older more primitive but indispensable 'brain', the cerebellum.

# GETTING TO KNOW YOU

The average human brain (Figure 9) weighs 1.5 kg (3.3 lbs). Einstein's brain, at 1.23 kg (2.71 lbs), was a trifle below par. But though brain size is crucial, our great advantage is the *number* of nerve cells (neurons) in our brains. And *where they're located*. Your brain contains 86 billion nerve cells, plus an even larger number of more ordinary *glial* cells that support and protect them.

The **cerebrum** comprises some 80% of your brain. It contains both grey and white matter. Its two hemispheres, connected by a fibrous rope, govern opposite sides of your body. Each hemisphere has four lobes.

The **cerebral cortex** is the cerebrum's outer layer. This wrinkly, folded clump of 16 billion nerve cells is your grey matter: the cells that make your brain different from that of other other primates. Because there are more of them, *and they are more intricately connected.*

The **cerebellum** or 'little brain' keeps you balanced and standing up straight. Surprisingly, it has billions more nerve cells than your cerebrum. But these have far fewer connections.

The **brain stem**, often called our 'reptilian brain', is a relay station between brain and body. It controls your vital, involuntary functions: breathing, heart rate, temperature, sleep cycles, digestion.

## Nerve cell (neuron)

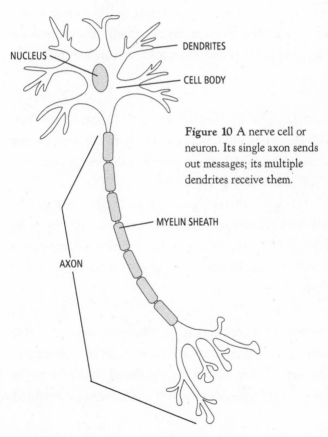

NUCLEUS

DENDRITES

CELL BODY

**Figure 10** A nerve cell or neuron. Its single axon sends out messages; its multiple dendrites receive them.

MYELIN SHEATH

AXON

# I'm nervous

*Nerve cells (neurons)* enable the brain to get its act together. They make up the highways, byways and spaghetti junctions that connect sense organs to your brain, muscles, and each other.

Nerve cells have an *electrical aspect*. This means they can talk. They send out messages from, say, toe to brain and back, and also to each other. They post thousands of messages every second. A single neuron can have 10,000 links. The entire neural grid has some 100 trillion. Facebook and Twitter are molasses.

Brains need energy. They use the equal of a low, 20-watt light bulb. Given how much work they do, that's a pretty green use of electricity. But it's also a quarter of the energy your body needs, so in that respect it's a lot.

Although different areas of the brain specialise in particular processes, *several areas are always involved in any action*. When you pick up a pencil, for instance, trillions of nerves network to make it happen. Trillions more kick in when you begin to write.

**The neural network** Long thread-like fibres extend from each nerve cell's body, as shown in Figures 10 and 11. They are your *white matter*. Each neuron has one thread *(axon)* for output and several threads *(dendrites)* for input. Axons are insulated, like electrical wires. The myelin sheath protects against nerve damage and most probably increases efficiency.

Electric impulses zoom along the threads, leaping from one neuron to another, towards their destinations. Many are on a return trip, going from a stubbed toe to the brain, for instance; then back again, so that you can feel it.

The neurons never touch each other. A chemical *neurotransmitter* ferries electrical signals across narrow gaps between the neurons. These are called *synapses*. (See Figure 11 inset)

## Nerve cell (neuron)

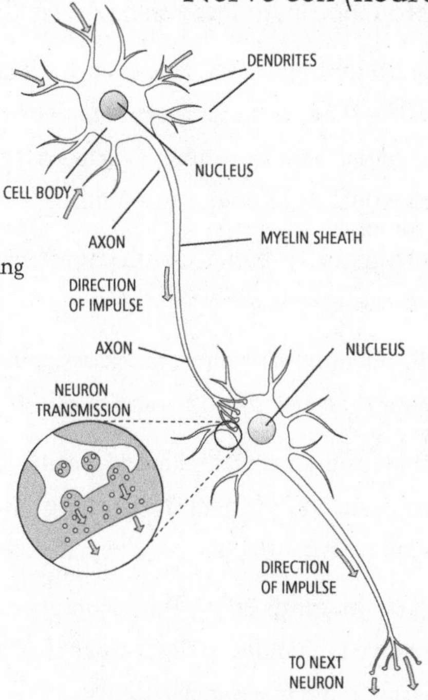

DENDRITES

NUCLEUS

CELL BODY

AXON

MYELIN SHEATH

**Figure 11** Interacting neurons. Messages must cross the gaps between nerve endings, as the inset shows.

DIRECTION OF IMPULSE

AXON

NUCLEUS

NEURON TRANSMISSION

DIRECTION OF IMPULSE

TO NEXT NEURON

# BRAIN FUNCTIONS

**CEREBRUM** contains both grey and white matter. The **cerebral cortex** is the *grey matter* that forms the cerebrum's outer layer. Its 4 lobes, illustrated on page 93, specialise and interact as follows:

**Frontal lobe** – thinking, planning, problem solving, movement, emotions (*Broca's area*), self-awareness, impulse control.

**Parietal lobe** integrates sensory input, spatial and visual perception.

**Occipital lobe** interprets vision.

**Temporal lobe** interprets sensory input. Important for orientation, navigation, language comprehension (Wernicke's area), memory storage, learning. Includes the **limbic system**: the emotional brain, unique to mammals. *It has 4 areas:*

> **Amygdala** – associated with emotions; famously fear, but also empathy.
>
> **Hippocampus** receives, processes and transmits information. Stores memories and recalls them when needed.
>
> **Thalamus** – central relay and sorting station between the brain and 4 senses (not hearing). Involved in regulating consciousness, sleep, alertness.
>
> **Hypothalamus** controls involuntary nervous system. Involved in emotion, sleep–wake rhythmns. Links nervous and hormonal systems.

**MIDBRAIN** exerts motor control of seeing and hearing, sleep and alertness.

**CEREBELLUM** coordinates voluntary movement, posture, balance using input from eyes, ears, muscles.

**BRAIN STEM** includes pons and medulla. Connects brain and spinal cord, relays information between brain and body. Important in controlling blood pressure, breathing. Involved in sleep.

**Pons** – motor control, sensory analysis, sleep, balance.

**Medulla** oversees breathing, heartbeat.

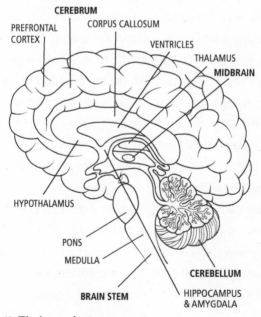

**Figure 12** The human brain cross section.

# BRINGING UP BABY

A human foetus makes twice the neurons it will ever need. Four weeks after conception, 250,000 neurons a minute are being formed. But few of them interconnect. The connections, vital for future stability, will be made by early emotional bonding and experiences.

A pruning of surplus nerve endings starts in the womb. What's left depends on what is being used. Use it or lose it, as the saying goes. It's a competitive business meant to strengthen remaining connections.

With puberty, another huge shake-up occurs – literally a nervous breakdown and make over, in which personality is remoulded. Adolescence is a kind of metamorphosis, like the change from caterpillar to butterfly. In addition to the physical changes sex hormones produce, myriad other hormone-driven changes are going on inside the brain, especially in the *limbic system* and, most especially, in the *amygdala* (your so-called 'emotional brain'). Driven by streaming hormones, about half of extant neuron connections get pruned. Again, stronger remaining connections is the goal.

Risk-taking, rage, aggression, fear, excitement, ad-dictions, thrill-seeking, impulsiveness, peer approval, social anxiety, self-centredness, embarrassment, idealism, misreading of social cues, instant gratification, eating and sleeping habits – all are affected in adolescence.

Unfortunately, the *prefrontal cortex*, a small area in your forehead, responsible for planning, moderation and decision-making, is the last bit of the brain to mature. Teenagers are at the mercy of capricious limbic systems, and parents must, when possible, stand in for tardy prefrontal cortexes.

But by age 25, the prefrontal cortex usually has hold of the reins. The young adult bursts from its chrysalis. Physical and mental powers peak. Original ideas and extraordinary accomplishments are suddenly possible. At age 26, Albert Einstein delivered classical physics' first big body blow. By 25, Alexander the Great had pocketed much of the known world, and aged 21, college dropout Steve Jobs co-founded Apple.

These are precious moments. For, having peaked, the downslide has already begun. Gradually, some neurons will die off, memory's acuity will decline, sight and hearing dim and the likelihood of dementia rise. The lights are slowly going out.

# STATES OF MIND

**Mind** is a spectrum of moods involving consciousness, higher faculties and emotions. Some see it as a sort of workaday soul.

No mental state ever lasts. Events, doused by hormones or drugs, move the barometer up and down a wide selection of moods. The deep grief of bereavement, the pleasure of doing a good deed, the bliss of falling in love and the heightened sense that turns a feeling of oneness with the universe into ecstasy, are all hormone or drug-induced states of mind.

The hormones involved are mostly positive in effect. *Endorphins* are the body's opiates. (Its receptors also welcome morphine, which can block the body's own feel-good secretions.) *Dopamine* and *serotonin* are reward-givers and feel-good facilitators. Their 'highs' are triggered by exercise and successful endeavour. *Oxytocin*, a famously social hormone, strengthens emotional ties. It bonds mother and baby, boy and girl, and helps to bond friendships. *Cortisol* is a stress hormone, a product of fight, freeze or flight instincts. An overdose can cause anxiety and depression.

**Consciousness** is a mystery, a fact, an illusion, a mind thinking about itself, a way of talking about things. It's under debate. But it's generally agreed you need to be awake, aware of your surroundings, and have a notion of who you are.

When fully conscious, you know you know things. You can hold thoughts in your head and make plans around them, form relationships and create things like paintings, start-ups, mathematical equations and computers. Consciousness helps dissolve conflict and make considered choices.

A growing awareness of animal consciousness is blurring a long-held belief in our exclusivity. Monkeys and squirrels crack tough nuts with stones. Crows fashion hooked twigs to tease out insects and worms. They can also remember your face. Wolf packs organise and communicate to pick out and take down much bigger prey than themselves. Amazingly, Australian kites and falcons will snatch a burning stick from a bushfire, carry it off in their beaks, and start a new fire elsewhere to force prey into the open.

We are not more wide-awake or better at perceiving our surroundings than other animals. In fact, the reverse is true. Consciousness may be a matter of degree.

**Thinking vs. feeling** What's the difference? It's pretty obvious on the face of it: you feel with your fingers and you think with your brain. No, you do both with your brain.

Thoughts and feelings are electro-chemical reactions. Thoughts are conscious ways of dealing with needs that feelings express. A thought can be rethought and thought about. It can invoke a feeling and vice versa. It's crucial in solving problems and developing off-the-cuff ideas, like a new bottle opener or how to harness neutrinos. Most creative 'thinking' is unconscious.

**Sleep** Spending a third of your life asleep is anything but a waste of time. Sleep is a state of unconsciousness, but during it the brain labours on. Sleep cycles last roughly 90 minutes and they have 2 forms: NREM (non-rapid eye movement) or deep sleep, and REM (rapid eye movement), when eyes flit back and forth, as they normally do. REM sleep is dream time. It occurs in all mammals and birds. The body is paralysed but the brain is highly active.

Sleep consolidates memories and, in doing so, makes room for new ones. It's important in learning, invention, physical and mental well-being. Sleep 'knits up the ravelled sleeve of care' and is 'chief nourisher in life's feast'. Once again, Shakespeare's uncanny intuition is spot-on.

# CAN DO

**Intelligence** has been described as adaptability to a wide variety of events. In other words, the ability to manage pretty well whatever life throws at you. As the ultimate survival tool, intelligence depends on a combination of nerve cell density, hormonal balance, a healthy metabolism, and of course the brain's input. Language skills are a big bonus. In short: genes provide the equipment, experience informs it and language oils the wheels.

*Genius* appears to be a sort of lopsided intelligence: a brain capable of unusually strong concentration in a particular direction. Often, it's at the expense of other abilities, like social cues, as frequently seen in Asperger's syndrome.

**Memories** are physically encoded and stored impressions capable of retrieval. There are two types: conscious and unconscious memory. *Unconscious memory* involves learned actions: playing the cello, riding a skateboard, operating a smart phone. All must be reinforced by practice if they're to last.

*Conscious memory* is recalled experiences and events: first love, the taste of a cookie, the idea you had recently for an online blog. Without conscious memory, verbal language, meaning and past experience wouldn't be possible.

But conscious memory is tricky. Bits of a single memory are stored in different parts of the brain, either in brain cells or their synapses. (It's under debate.) Linked by association, on recall, the different bits must be reassembled, like a jigsaw puzzle. This could be why, *whenever* you pull one up, it's slightly changed. This really happens every time.

Memories are strongly reinforced by feelings. The Renaissance sculptor, Benvenuto Cellini's autobiography opens with his earliest memory. The family are sitting around the fireplace when suddenly they see a salamander in the flames. A rare and marvellous sight, with mythical associations. The boy is thrilled. Abruptly, his father, leaning forward, slaps him. 'Now you'll always remember you saw a salamander in the fire,' he rightly says.

When ageing sets in, memories begin to mimic Humpty Dumpty. But the more associations a memory has, the firmer it's likely to be anchored. Proper names are usually the first to go. Tom, Dick and Harriet are poorly moored compared with Crazy Horse, Black Cloud and Sitting Bull. Something potential parents may wish to consider.

Memories are crucial to all activity. They can give pleasure or pain, but *they are not true records of the past.*

**Free will**, the ability to act freely and make up your own mind is another self-aggrandising illusion. In addition to being influenced from without, we're influenced from within in ways beyond our understanding or ability to change. Neuroscience has kindled a rethink of our proud notion of free will. The debate helps keep philosophy on the boil.

## To summarise:

- In Chapter 5, your body's cells were compared to a federation of Lilliput-like states, under your imperial rule. To extend the simile, your cerebral cortex is the royal residence of Your Supreme Consciousness (one of many honorary titles).

- Provincial rulers live in the palace too. They rule their own domains, but being neatly penned up, you can keep an eye on them, and they are at your beck and call.

- Whether you spend the day reading Proust or watching daytime TV, going to pop concerts or, dressed to the nines, lolling about with the likes of Madame de Montespan, the court bubbles with activities of its own. Each faction has its own regional interests. Quarrels can break out within factions and between different factions. The fractiousness never stops, as factions compete for influence, supremacy and your imperial attention. Nothing is done without a lot of to-do.

- When you deign to consult your court, an organised deliberation gets underway. But even then the rivalry never stops. The desire to do one another down, get your attention and have their own way, affects the advice they give you.

- You listen to them or you don't. They live in the dark; you are the sun king. The decision is ultimately yours, and you will take all the credit – especially when it's a good one, as it so often is. But the truth is it's Your Supreme Consciousness who's in the dark, a virtual figurehead controlled by a self-interested and rambunctious court. Nothing you can do is going to change it. You must all live together. So, it's best to face up to how things really are. Charles I got his head chopped off. You still have a palace, position, titles and innumerable perks.

# 10

# UP AND COMING

*'I have called this principle by which each slight variation, if useful, is preserved... Natural Selection.'*
Charles Darwin

Charles Darwin's book, *On the Origin of Species by Means of Natural Selection*, was published in 1859. The edition sold out on the same day and the world's mindset began to change for ever.

In his early twenties, Darwin had spent 5 years aboard ship as a naturalist, visiting South America, Australia and remote Pacific islands, in a round-the-world voyage. *Origin of Species* as it became known, derived from observations Darwin had made and thought about over decades. He was now 50 years old.

All living creatures struggle to survive in their habitat, he observed, and the fittest (i.e. the most successfully adapted to their surroundings) do so best. As a result, they have more offspring to pass their advantages on to. Ditto

*their* offspring, and so on. Over time, these minute but successful changes can modify a whole species – or create a new one.

In other words, a select few picked by nature in each
generation, according to their ability to survive, have over
millions of years evolved from a single ancestor into every
living creature on the planet.

God was nowhere in the picture.

The idea of *natural selection* had been bubbling up some
little while. An obscure Scottish gardener had reached
Darwin's conclusions 25 years earlier, and published them
in a wholly overlooked book on naval timber.

In 1844, an anonymously published book suggested
humans were descended from lesser primates. (The closet
author was a Scottish publisher whose firm sold Bibles.)
Alarmed by the outcry that this book provoked, Darwin's
own copious notes landed in a bottom drawer.

Fourteen years later, Darwin received an essay from a
young naturalist living in Borneo, Alfred Russel Wallace,
setting out views that closely paralleled Darwin's own.
Man and the hour had met. Darwin realised he must publish
or, scooped, be damned – to obscurity.

*The Origin of Species* caused a furore. Religious beliefs that for centuries had provided security, hope and

plausible explanations of existence began to crumble. So did humans' sense of their godlike superiority on the planet. 'Man is descended from a hairy, tailed quadruped, probably arboreal in its habits,' Darwin wrote.

For some, however, 'survival of the fittest', an up-by-the-bootstraps tale of social climbing right to the top, had a decided appeal. Unaware they were themselves dependent upon and crawling with bacteria, they took pride in having left their inferior forebears so very far behind. The Bible declared mankind should lord it over them, and they were happy to oblige.

## A closer look

In fact, Darwin's theory contained a gaping hole. For how did these improving changes, these *mutations*, get passed on?

Farmers had practised selective breeding for centuries, so it certainly happened. Darwin had seen some weird varieties of well-known birds on the isolated Galapagos Islands: cormorants that could no longer fly and finches that pecked other birds and sucked their blood. He believed some sort of parental blending might be at work.

In fact, Gregor Mendel (the monk who crossbred garden peas, see page 83), had a good part of the answer. He knew traits didn't blend. Rather, they were tiny pieces that, when shuffled about in reproduction, had dominant and recessive effects on offspring.

Darwin, unfortunately, hadn't heard of Mendel. But Mendel was aware of Darwin. And unimpressed by Darwin's notion of an inheritance melting pot, Mendel ignored him.

Everybody ignored Mendel. Only in 1900 did his work finally receive attention, and the word *gene* was coined to describe those mysterious specks that could mutate and pass traits on.

But what is the *cause* of mutations? We now know that it's mistakes in DNA (see Chapter 8). A mistake of one letter in the four-lettered genetic code changes the protein recipe. Like mistaking salt for sugar when sweetening your coffee.

So, tiny random mistakes, accumulating over millions of years, have been the making of us.


# FITTING IN

But gene mutation is only half the story, since whether a mutation is useful or not depends on its host's habitat.

Asteroids, ice, volcanos, earthquakes, floods and drought have repeatedly wreaked havoc on the earth. Climate changes altered temperature levels and with it the food supply. Entire species were wiped out. Others, better fitted to survive in the new conditions, replaced them.

Competition for food and sex (the instinct to pass genes on), together with female preferences, have also played big roles in evolution's direction. Ditto effective means of self-defence. (Every living thing is in a food chain, a life-threatening situation – unless you're a plant that can regenerate.)

Wings easily outpace legs, colours can camouflage and venom stun or kill. Eyes were such a success that they evolved several times independently. Biting, hooking, clawing, stinging, downright cunning, also size and muscles, can increase chances of survival long enough to pass genes on.

Weapons of mood evolved as well. Fear can make life miserable, but it goads a sharp lookout for danger. The other side of that coin is, of course, aggression. It's highly prized by species across the spectrum, e.g. snakes, sharks, hornets, tigers, gorillas, and you know who.

Male conflict is, whatever else, a genetic shakedown to produce the fittest. The ultimate shakedown, however, belongs to females. Females usually choose which (of the surviving) male genomes are, in their opinion, worth preserving.

*Human* males, exceptionally, refused to put up with this. Until recently, most women were either abducted or had their spouses chosen by their fathers. Some still do.

Females look for strength and health. They also fall for showy eye-catching stuff. Preening peacocks are a fine example. Antlers, useful for fight as well as show, fill a double bill. But growing a pair of trees on top of your head each year drains energy, even as it trumpets good health. Besides, when show-offs overdo it, nature will often put her foot down. The magnificently-branched Irish elk probably couldn't raise his head up from the water fast enough. He is now extinct.

Singing and dancing, perfume, extravagant plumage and brilliant colours embellish the mating game. Female choice has affected physical appearances. A sense of beauty seems to be hardwired, even if it differs in the eyes of different beholders. Peahen aesthetics are not those of the horned toad, though both exhibit a fondness for flamboyance.

## BACK STORY

Let's backtrack for a minute and take a look at the challenges of changing environments. When life first sprouted some 4 billion years ago there was almost no oxygen in the atmosphere nor any protection from the sun's ultra-violet radiation. Then, some 2 million years later, a group of primitive bacteria called *cyanobacteria* began to make the planet habitable. Cyanobacteria were literally the breath of life: they gave us oxygen, and still do!

Remember, plants make their own food, and almost everybody else's. As described in Chapter 2, they use water and chlorophyll to convert the sun's rays into carbohydrates, releasing oxygen in the process. This amazing feat of *photosynthesis* is achieved by tiny *chloroplasts* inside the plant. Chloroplasts are evolved cyanobacteria. Oxygen and food, plus the sheltering atmosphere that makes earth habitable, was and is plants' doing. We had better keep that in mind.

With plenty of oxygen on tap, evolution took off in all directions, wherever it could find a niche. Creatures protected in the oceans crawled on to dry land. (Later, some crawled back again.) Most of the basic types of organisms alive today already existed 540 million years ago. We know because they made a lasting impression – as fossils.

Three great *domains* of life: **bacteria**, **archaea** and **eukarya** (organisms with nuclear cells), have been subdivided into six *kingdoms*: **Bacteria, Archaea, Protists, Fungi, Plants and Animals**. Over 400 million years, 5 catastrophes wiped out the majority of living species. The most famous occurred 66 million years ago, when a huge asteroid slammed into Mexico's Yucatan peninsula. The resulting devastation killed off all the dinosaurs (except for birds).

This momentous event, mourned by children everywhere, allowed a few timid, nocturnal mammals to begin to make their way. We are their descendants.

# ME FIRST

Self-interest is life's prime mover, by default. But *self* has nuances. A sea sponge, probably the first animal to evolve, is just a bunch of loosely stuck together cells. Pull one apart and it makes no difference to any body part.

The Portuguese man o'war, with its long poisonous tentacles, is one step up. It's a bunch of four groups of organisms. Each group does a different job, so could no longer live independently.

Then there are the multi-bodied bodies, such as the ant and bee colonies. Although the queen bee and her serf sisters share their genes, their roles are fixed and different. The hive behaves as a single, loosely integrated body. The bees are its cells and the queen its nucleus. The hive is held together by hormonal glue.

We humans are highly social. We're quick to join in for food, fun and safety, as well as sex. We'll even risk self-destruction for the common good. But though keen on individuality, we, like the Portuguese man o'war, are too interdependent to survive for long alone.

# POST-DARWIN

Decoding DNA has put some new cards on evolution's table, and geneticists are busy adjusting the rules of the game. The new cards are called **horizontal gene transfers – HGT**, for short.

We now know bacteria can and do swap their free-floating genes. These 'jumping genes' could well have jump-started a primitive form of evolution. They continue to affect genomes today.

Since ancient times, *viruses* have picked up foreign genes and dumped them into others' genomes. Some 8 per cent of every human genome has viral links.

*DNA* misprinting can cause a gene to produce one or more extra copies of itself. Should a duplicated strand contain a useful mutation, that mutation could become a new gene. Or a new gene could split its function with its duplicate, and two new genes result. Repeated duplication explains how multiples of useful genes arose in genetic codes. We have 400 genes for smell; dogs have 800.

Whole chromosomes can also be duplicated. Down's syndrome is an example.

Despite these new-found complexities, Darwin's natural selection still holds true. For whatever a gene's origin may be, usefulness will decide its future in a genome.

## POST-PARTUM

Evolution can take millions of years, as when a new species evolves. But it can also happen quickly. In under a century, pigeons and moths turned smoky grey to blend in with city smog. And bacteria's super-fast replication can turn out an antibiotic-resistant strain in hours.

❁

## The Tree of Life

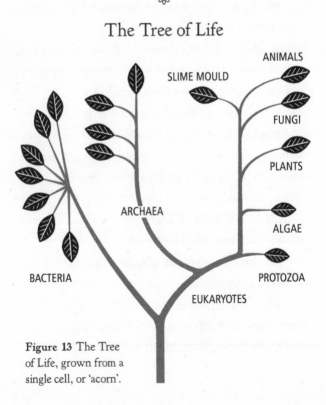

**Figure 13** The Tree of Life, grown from a single cell, or 'acorn'.

It's taken us eons to get to where we are today. But where is that? Animals are a minor branch on the evolutionary tree and we humans a mere twig on the animal branch, as shown in Figure 13. Yet we have vastly superior brains. We can, to a unique degree, control our environment, and we're beginning to control our genes. We are fit, we are powerful, we are creative and we are dangerous. To celebrate the fact, we've axed the old, archaic ancestral tree; lopped off its limbs and fashioned a more fitting and original work of art: the image of a magnificent totem pole, with ourselves smugly enthroned on the top.

## To summarise:

- Evolution is driven by passing on the chance mutations of genes that have proved useful.

- What is useful depends on your environment.

- Mutations are caused by mistakes in DNA. These are sparked by chemicals, radiation, old age and, significantly, viruses.

- Bacteria's ability to swap genes, and viruses' ability to carry them around, have had a significant role in evolution.

- Competition, ideas of beauty and powers of defence have also influenced the course of evolution.

# FIVE MASS EXTINCTIONS

| | |
|---|---|
| **Ordovician–Silurian** | 439 million years ago, 86% extinction |
| **Late Devonian** | 364 million years ago, 75% extinction |
| **Permian–Triassic** | 251 million years ago, 96% extinction |
| **Triassic–Jurassic** | 201 million years ago, dinosaurs reign |
| **Cretaceous-Paleogene** | 66 million years ago, 76% extinction. |

# TIMELINE OF LIFE

(Dates are ballpark figures)

| | |
|---|---|
| **3.8 billion years ago** | Primitive microbes appear. Last universal common ancestor of all cells living today (LUCA) |
| **3.7 billion years ago** | Oldest fossils found |

| | |
|---|---|
| **3.6 billion years ago** | Viruses probably around |
| **2.6 billion years ago** | Cyanobacteria create photosynthesis |
| **1.6 billion years ago** | Cell with nucleus containing DNA |
| **1.1 billion years ago** | First sexually producing organisms |
| **800 million years ago** | Simple cell clusters emerge |
| **700 million years ago** | Soft bodied multicellular life |
| **640 million years ago** | First animals: sponges |
| **630 million years ago** | Organisms have symmetry: up, down, left, right; their size increases |
| **540 million years ago** | Rise in oxygen, end of glaciers. Basic body plans emerge |
| **530 million years ago** | Backbones (vertebrates) develop |
| **475–400 million years ago** | Land plants and diversity of living creatures |
| **400–360 million years ago** | Insects, spiders, millipedes, fungi |

| 370 million years ago | First amphibians and four-legged animals |
|---|---|
| 320 million years ago | First reptiles |
| 225 million years ago | Dinosaurs |
| 200 million years ago | First mammals |
| 150 million years ago | First birds |
| 140 million years ago | First flowering plants, also insects and bees |
| 75 million years ago | Ancestors of primates and rodents split. They still share half their genes. |
| 66 million years ago | Asteroid explosion kills all dinosaurs, except birds. Small mammals begin to thrive |
| 65–38 million years ago | Placental mammals, whales, bats, diversity of birds and plants |
| 55 million years ago | First primates |
| 15 million years ago | Great apes split from gibbon ancestors |
| 11–7 million years ago | Chimpanzees and humans split but share 98% of genes |
| 315,000 years ago | First modern humans, *Homo sapiens*, appear |

# 11

# MEET THE ANCESTORS

*'Always remember that you are absolutely unique,*
*just like everyone else.'* Margaret Mead

One day a few early apes climbed down from the trees and loped off inquisitively to have a look around. They were adaptable in all respects. Time passed. As they crossed the open savannahs, they began to walk upright, balancing on the wrists of their hind legs. Their brains ballooned, their legs lengthened to fit an ambitious stride. And what had become arms, shortened to better control strong new grasping hands that could greet challengers with a proper fist.

They were the chosen ones, the select few – their genes the crown jewels to be passed on to the best and brightest of their descendants.

As time went on, all who were unable to keep pace or in good stead fell, one way or another, by the wayside, in the long march of the fittest into history. Until eventually the selected few stood alone. Nothing remained to connect them to their ancient forebears, hooting nervously from the trees at the approach of Adam and Eve.

# BIG GAME HUNTING

Darwin's *Origin of Species* had overturned the Bible's creation myth, and the hunt was on to find the 'missing link' that connected man to ape and would confirm his world-shaking theory.

A fossilised part-skeleton, found a few years earlier (1856) in Germany's Neander valley, was dusted off and declared to be a new hominid species: *Neanderthal*. It would eventually be dated 400,000 years old.

Fossils of vaguely ape- or human-like bones, previously rare, began to be dug up in Africa, which was declared the cradle of humankind. The fossilised bones, teeth and skulls were studiously catalogued, using an eighteenth-century classification system of Phylum, Order, Family, Genus, Species.

**Genus *Homo*** comprised both modern and archaic humans, or *hominins*, as they're called today. To qualify as a hominin, at least one anatomical feature found in humans, but *not* in chimpanzees, was needed. A further subdivision into **Species** roughly defined groups that were unable to interbreed and produce offspring.

Three early hominin discoveries proved pivotal: **handy man** (*Homo habilis*), **standing man** (*Homo erectus*) and **Lucy** (*Homo australopithecus*).

The fossilised remains of **handy man** (*Homo habilis*) were discovered in 1960, along with the crudely flaked stone tools that gave the species its name. At 2.4 million years old handy man is, thus far, the earliest toolmaker and oldest member of genus *Homo*.

The fossilised bones of **standing man** (*Homo erectus*), had been found in Java, back in 1891. This tall, sturdy, heavy-browed, chinless biped might equally have been dubbed 'walking man'. The first known hominin to leave Africa, standing man's fossils have turned up in Europe, East Asia and Siberia, as well as Indonesia. The 1.8 million-year-old species was still alive 200,000 years ago.

As the longest surviving early hominin species, and the most humanlike, eating meat may partly account for *Homo erectus'* enlarged brain, improved stone tools and enormous stamina. Males were bigger than females, showing divided labour had become the norm. Most probably, we ourselves (plus several other hominin species) are *Homo erectus'* descendants.

In 1973, the fossilised skeleton of a small archaic female, half-ape half-human, was discovered in northern Kenya, causing a world sensation. The unsteady little biped had big teeth, long arms reaching to her knees (useful for climbing trees), humanlike feet and a chimp-sized brain. She pushed evolution back an incredible 3.5 *million* years. Named **Lucy**, after the Beatles' song, 'Lucy in the Sky with Diamonds', she soon became part of a new genus, earlier than *Homo*, called *Australopithecus*.

The genus contained distinctly primitive, yet vaguely humanlike creatures who had lived in southern Africa. All had big teeth, chimp-sized brains, a low heavily ridged brow and projecting but chinless lower faces. They could walk upright, but their short legs and long arms made

## Evolution of the skull

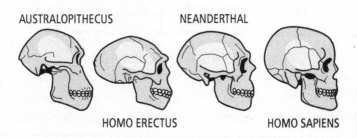

Figure 14 Skull evolution

them more at home in trees. (Though Lucy seems to have died falling from one.)

Today, hominin fossils are turning up on a regular basis. In the last 30 years, more than 20 new species have been unearthed, helping to fill the 7 or so million-year-gap since we branched off from the chimpanzees, with whom we share 98% of our genes.

What's more, ancient hominins are giving up their ghosts. Fossils up to 50,000 years old are being reliably dated, using *carbon 14 decay* and a more recent process, *uranium lead decay*, that can reveal much older dates. (See page 197). This growing ability to test evidence using technology is helping to make anthropology a science in the true sense of the word.

It's now known that DNA can stay in fossils long after an organism has died. As a result, geneticists have begun to read hominin autobiographies. The story unfolds, they say, like an exciting thriller, as new pages are translated, new chapters assembled, and the plot continues to thicken.

The established view of human evolution as a single-file of increasingly humanlike creatures morphing into us, is in the dustbin. The truth is more like a ratatouille. We now know several hominin species were alive at the same time. And they were interbreeding.

# THE MISFITS

Ironically, some of the oldest fossils are among the most recently found. Some may even have been 'living fossils' when they were alive, most notably, the so-called 'hobbits' and *Homo naledi*.

**Hobbits** (*Homo floresiensis*): In 2003, fossilised bones of tiny ape-like creatures were found on the Indonesian island of Flores. The height of four-year-olds, their infant-sized heads had a ridged brow typical of *Homo erectus*. But other, more primitive features resembled earlier *Australopithecus*. (They were dubbed hobbits after the pint-sized humanlike creatures in J. R. R. Tolkien's *Lord of the Rings*.)

Million-year-old stone tools were found beside the skeletons, together with other tools only 50,000 years old. Some hobbit fossils have now been dated 700,000 years old.

That these truly archaic beings were still alive and kicking 50,000 years ago, as their tools indicate, mightily screwed up the standard model of evolving humans. The paleo-world was riven by disputes and feathers began to fly. Many experts refused to accept the hobbits as a new species, claiming they were diseased or dwarfs. Others suggested they had descended from handy man (*H. habilis*), who apparently had never left Africa.

Despite the hobbits' minute size, standing man (*H. erectus*) is currently the favoured fit. This was boosted by another recent find. Fossil skulls dug up in Dmanisi, Georgia, and dated 1.8 million years old, are believed to be an archaic version of *Homo erectus*. This caused speculation that *Homo erectus* may have originated in Eurasia, trotted off to Africa when the climate deteriorated, and wisely returned again when it improved.

Very recently, stone tools over two million years old have turned up in China. The date, not far behind handy man's African tools, helps support theories that hominins originated, not in Africa, but in the East. Also that hominin interbreeding was much earlier and far more widespread than was previously believed.

***Homo naledi***: In 2013, two young explorers wriggled into a hidden pit deep inside a cave near Johannesburg, South Africa. To their astonishment, they found a lot of fossilised bones sticking up out of the floor. When examined, the bones showed a crazy mix of anatomical features. Part handy man (curved fingers, primitive shoulder and hip joints), the hands, legs and foot bones were akin to modern humans'.

At 300,000 years old, and far from the oldest hominin discovered, Naledi could still be the most primitive species in the entire *Homo* genus. A knockout blow to orderly evolutionary ladders and upward branching ancestral trees.

# KISSING KIN

**Neanderthals** have come in from the cold in every sense. Originating in Africa, they migrated to Europe about 450,000 years ago, probably along the Horn of Africa's coast and into Eurasia. Branching north and west, they endured the last Ice Age, only to be cold-shouldered eons later by their modern kin as low-browed dumbos, one step up from knuckle-walkers and nothing really to do with us.

But that would change.

Powerfully built, with brains slightly larger than ours, Neanderthals were formidable big game hunters of mammoths, rhinos and bison. They had carefully flaked stone tools and shafted-spears for close-range stabbing, the stone heads cleverly glued on with hot birch pitch. They fished, trapped birds, built lean-to shelters made with pegs and posts, and made use of fire for light, warmth and cooking. They wore animal skins softened to pliancy with their teeth and ornamented themselves with shell necklaces and ochre body paint. They played bone flutes and had a go at painting abstract symbols on the walls of caves. Most important, they enjoyed the power of speech (as other hominins probably did too).

The Neanderthals also buried their dead. Flowers found at one Neanderthal burial site suggest ritual, herbal acumen and maybe the idea of an afterlife.

In 2010, in a truly remarkable achievement, the entire Neanderthal genome was decoded. It revealed a close kinship to ourselves. Indeed, we may soon be the same species. In a way we already are. Not only do we share 99% of our genomes with Neanderthals (one percentage point more than we share with chimpanzees), we carry, on average, between 1% and 4% *specifically* Neanderthal genes. Amongst other things, they affect skin and hair colour, height, sense of smell and, significantly, immune systems.

Inheriting immunity from local diseases would have been a boon to recently-arrived European immigrants. It can still give protection today. A tendency for blood clotting, depression and type 2 diabetes are some of the downside features.

The astonishing news is that 50% of the Neanderthal genome remains with us, today. (Individuals carry only a small percentage of specifically Neanderthal genes, but we don't all carry the same ones.)

Neanderthals' last known refuge seems to have been southern Spain, some 40,000 years ago.

**Denisovans** In 2010, DNA was extracted from a child's fossilised finger bone, found in the Denisova Cave, in Siberia. It belonged to an unknown species, but one closely related to Neanderthals. Denisovan and Neanderthal lineages seem to have split about 750,000 years ago. Then 500,000 years later they got together again, and interbred.

Little fossil evidence exists so far, but we know Denisovan territory was widespread. East Asians, Indonesians and Australasians carry some of their genes. Tibetans can live at high altitudes thanks to one of them.

***Homo sapiens*** The earliest modern human remains discovered so far are 300,000 years old and were found in Morocco. The earliest modern European human remains, a skull fragment recently found in Greece, was dated 90,000 years later. Quite a gap, and we'll get back to it.

Hominin history is undergoing a big rethink. The developing story is a confusing mix of interbreeding and evolving anatomies – trial runs in nature's laboratory, where species emerged, overlapped, interbred and, for whatever reasons, disappeared. Disease and climate changes will have played a big part. But the extinction of so many hominin species – *Neanderthals*, *naledi*, *hobbits* and *erectus* – roughly coinciding with our arrival in their territories, has raised more than a few eyebrows.

# OLYMPIANS

'It seems to me,' wrote Darwin, 'that man with all his noble qualities ... still bears in his bodily frame the indelible stamp of his lowly origin.'

In other words, our differences aren't of substance but of degree. Our teeth are smaller, our gut is shorter, our legs are longer. We lack a brow ridge and we usually have a chin. We have larger, rounder heads and flatter faces, torsos that enable upright posture, and opposable thumbs that make for easier pickings and a better grip on hammers, needles and handshakes.

Our crowning glory is of course our brain. But that too is a matter of degree. It's a scaled-up primate brain. As seen in Chapter 9, the vast number of nerve cells packed into your cerebral cortex and their trillions of connections are what make the difference. And the difference is truly phenomenal.

# One up

In the seven or more million years since we parted company with chimpanzees and bonobos, our brains have tripled in size. Theirs have remained the same. Why is that?

In the thousands of generations that saw hominins' bodies transformed by genetic mistakes and environmental changes, lifestyles barely budged. Why is that?

Apart from verbal language, stone weapons and tools, bone needles and self-decoration, only one other significant innovation has survived.

Lightning strikes a tree. The tree is consumed, exuding at the same time a fiery heat. What a startling impression that must have made. In mythology, fire is a gift from the gods. Stealing an ember was treachery, an eternal flame a practical and sacred necessity.

In addition to light, warmth and keeping wild animals at bay – ergo, making life more comfortable – fire sparked cooking.

**Cooking** is believed to have begun around a million years ago. It roughly coincided with rapid brain development. As already mentioned, *H. erectus* may have been the first hominin to cook food.

Cooking yields more calories. It also eases digestion, and chewing it takes less energy. Guts began to shorten and teeth got smaller.

Humans need about 2,000 calories a day and your brain consumes a quarter of those. Other vertebrate brains use only 10%. For eons, evolution chose brawn over brain.

With the arrival of cooking, several physical changes took place. The large teeth and thick-boned skulls with heavy muscles attached, necessary for chewing raw food, began to disappear, resulting in the flatter modern face. Time spent chewing the fat was freed up for other things. Suddenly, there was time and energy to spare. And yet, surprisingly, no other lasting innovations appeared, except the bow and arrow, until the clay cookpot emerged in China, 15,000 to 12,000 years ago. (It took another 6,000 years or so for it to go west.)

Maybe there was no need. A nomadic hunter-gatherer lifestyle suited human nature. It was tailor-made: what humans had evolved to do best. And when something works, we – and also nature – want to repeat it.

With more energy, better memory and communication skills, hunting methods vastly improved. Sneaky scavenging was probably abandoned. Mammoths, bison and rhinos made more respectable challenges. Pursuing them sent our ancestors striding across the earth, surely revelling in the intoxicating thrill of exploration and un-bridled freedom, as their mastery of the world began!

## Moving on

Assuming the earliest hominin migrations in and out of Africa were down to *Homo erectus*, some two million years ago, and the first *Homo sapiens* migrations happened around 350,000 years ago (but left no sign genetically), a lot of toing and froing probably took place in between. And with it, a good deal of interbreeding.

Genetic data suggests that today's entrenched popu-lations outside Africa descended from a small single group of modern humans who arrived in the Middle East about 66,000 years ago. Nomadic big-game hunters, following animal trails, some of them moved west into Europe, and shared Neanderthal territory. For 20–30,000 years these dark-skinned, blue-eyed modern humans (mitochondrial haplogroup U5) dominated Europe.

Then, about 9,000 years ago, farmers from the Middle East arrived in Europe. Genetic data show they didn't mix much with the nomadic hunter-gatherers, the U5s, who today form less than 10% of European and American populations. (I'm one, with an add-on of 2.6% Neanderthal genes.)

About 4,500 years ago, yet another wave of migrants, the Yamnaya, spread across Europe, this time from the Russian steppes. Herdsmen and fierce warriors, they had horses and wagons. And they made a lasting impression. The Yamnaya brought with them the basis of all the Indo-European languages spoken today. They also left their genes. The local male DNA vanished and Yamnaya DNA replaced it. Female mitochondrial DNA stayed the same. You get the picture.

Early migrations to the **Americas** most likely involved Asians crossing the then extant land bridge (which disappeared about 10,000 years ago) and eventually following the west coast south by foot or boat. The earliest human presence in the Americas has recently been dated to 33,000 years ago. But a recent discovery of crushed mammoth bones, in San Diego, California, suggests a human presence 120,000 years ago. If true, Neanderthals, Denisovans or some unknown 'ghost species', tracking bison across the land bridge, could have been the first Americans.

**Australia** was settled about 65,000 years ago. Indigenous genomes show, on average, 5% Denisovan genes.

## To summarise:

- Modern humans (*Homo sapiens*) evolved from a mix of earlier species, notably *H. erectus*, that interbred and eventually became extinct.

- Development of a large complex brain coincided with the practice of cooking food.

- The Neanderthal genome has been decoded. Everyone descended from populations outside Africa carries a bit of it (not the same bit).

- New fossil discoveries, technical dating processes and scientific analysis of fossil DNA are causing prehistory to be rewritten and archaeology to be accepted as an established science.

# PRIMATE CHRONOLOGY

(*NB. These are ballpark figures.* **mya** = *millions of years ago*)

| | |
|---|---|
| **55 mya** | first primates emerge |
| **15 mya** | great apes split from gibbon ancestors |
| **8 mya** | chimps and humans split from gibbon ancestors |
| **7–5 mya** | date of earliest fossils of hominin ancestors: 'Toumai' or *Sahelanthropus tchadensis*, found in Chad, oldest specimen to date |
| **3.3 mya** | earliest stone tools (simple pebbles and flaked, recently found in Kenya) |
| **2.5 mya** | crude stone tools found with *H. habilis* fossils |
| **1.85 mya** | the modern hand developed |
| **1.6 mya** | hand axes in use |
| **1 mya** | cooking and rapid brain growth transform human life |
| **750,000 years ago** | first Neanderthals |

| 500,000 years ago | Neanderthals and modern humans split |
|---|---|
| 400,000 years ago | Denisovans split from Neanderthals |
| 315,000 years ago | date of earliest *H. sapiens* fossil, found in Morocco. Sophisticated flaked stone tools made by *H. sapiens* and Neanderthals |
| 210,000 years ago | fossil skull of *Homo sapiens*, found in Greece. Human brains stop growing |
| 66,000 years ago | modern humans migrate from Africa and begin to populate Europe and Asia. (Earlier *Homo sapiens* arrivals disappeared) |
| 65,000 years ago | modern humans arrive in north Australia |
| 40,000 years ago | modern humans arrive in Europe |
| 44,000 years ago | earliest cave murals, found in Indonesia |
| 33,000 years ago | modern humans arrive in Northwest America |
| 15,000 years ago | clay cooking pots made in East Asia |
| 7,000 years ago | clay cooking pots made in Europe, Africa and Americas |

# 12

# CULTURED APES

*'Reginald considered that the Duchess had much to learn; in particular, not to hurry out of the Carlton as though afraid of losing one's last bus.'*
H. H. Munro, *Tales of Saki*

Bonding is fundamental in nature: the strong nuclear force holds atomic nuclei together, chemical bonds hold molecules together, sticky proteins hold cells together and culture holds people together. But compared to nature's superglues, cultural glues are water-based pastes that often need reinforcement. This has its advantages, as will be seen.

Culture refers to social behaviour inside a group. Evolution's propeller spins out multitudes of species whose social behaviour is largely expressed by innate 'hardwired' instincts. Safety in numbers is a good example. Shoals, swarms, flocks and herds manage by moving in sync, as if single-bodied beings. This lowers the odds of being attacked. For us, however, this 'herd instinct' is flexible. We can choose to peel off, leave the others behind and go our own way. Of course, manoeuvring outside the box can be dangerous. But the upside is that flexibility makes it easier to adapt to new situations. It's even possible that early humans who veered off, and survived to pass on their genes, spawned our own instinct for independence. Highly valued today, it's also a cultural thorn.

Modern human culture aims to blend individual and group interests into a smoothly pasted, superior collage called civilisation. Morality is its self-governing mechanism, virtue its badge of success. Rules and laws press the reluctant back into the mould.


## BACK STORY

Human culture probably developed from the need to look after babies. A fish pops out of its egg and swims off. A colt is on its legs in hours and a bird gets pushed from the nest in days. A human baby is a feeble tadpole sort of creature. But if it were born any later, its head size would mean it wouldn't be born at all.

Babies arrive with strong instincts. Vociferously signalling moods and basic needs, they're soon walking upright, running, jumping and playing with other children. But a lot of physical and mental development lies ahead. In addition to body growth, fitting into the modern mould means years of creeping snail-like to school, and, where possible, learning the ropes in a stable environment.

Most likely, children gave life meaning, as well as families their potential power. Female fertility was idolised in carved voluptuous figures, of a sort obtained today by too many visits to McDonald's. The more children, the stronger and safer the family. If large enough it could extend into kinship-based clans and, eventually, become a tribe.

Tribes improved and controlled mating options, safety, food supplies and fun. The price tag was, and is, being agreeable. Thinking and acting like others, submitting to an authority or the majority, even sacrificing one's life for the group's good: *dulce et decorum est pro patria mori*.[2]

Domestic chores made female bonding an everyday need, and gossip a favourite glue. In return for ready sex, men promised protection and brought home the bacon. Hunting and warfare required tight social bonds, plus a fixed chain of command. But its glue rarely outlasted the event. (Moreover, the bigger the group the weaker its glue.)

---

[2] 'It is sweet and fitting to die for your country.' The Roman poet Horace's line of praise was used with heavy irony in Wilfred Owen's poem describing the horrors of trench warfare in the First World War.

Early humans often regarded animals as superior beings, which in the wild they mostly were. They can run faster, see sharper, hear better and smell more keenly. Many are bigger and stronger than us, and some of them can fly. All arrive in ready-made clothes and are usually quick to look after themselves.

Keen to acquire such advantageous traits, we mimicked them, wearing animal masks, wrapping ourselves in their skins, and eating their flesh in hopes of acquiring their abilities. Eating, after all, transforms others' matter into ours. This sense of life's interconnectedness, intuitive in primitive societies, is pretty unusual today.

But the feature of our ballooning brains that made social life such a big success was, of course, verbal language.


## SPEAKEASY

All living things communicate. *Smells*, *sounds* and *gestures* are the available means. But *smell* is believed to be the oldest. It involves chemical signals, plus a nose or equivalent – sometimes it's a gene – to receive them. Hormones, especially *pheromones*, are used by plants, animals, insects, and also cells, to communicate. Their odours, released into the air or in fluids like urine, signal fertility, kinship, territory, fear – and possibly much more.

**Gesturing**, or body language, is widespread: chest beating, presenting a rosy bottom, strutting about shaking one's plumage or revealing honey's location with a wiggle dance, are examples. Shedding tears, smiling, laughing and pulling faces to express a mood are distinctly human. A wink, a shrug, a shaken fist, elbow poke or raised eyebrow are pretty much understood everywhere.

What's more, we're first-class mimics. Crucial to learning, miming conveys meaning by example. Just as early humans mimicked animals, children's play mimics grown-ups. It's thought that special *mirror neurons* in the brain may be at work. These fire when you perform an action. Amazingly, they also fire when you see someone else perform an action.

The jury is out on mirror neurons' importance, but the ability to divine others' intentions and imagine yourself in their shoes – to empathise – is the bedrock of human social life. Its absence is a feature of autism.

If animals' faces could clearly express their feelings, our relations with them would doubtless be very different.

Forests are cacophonies of **sound**. Calls, barks, yowls, roars and sing-song declare danger, mating desires, food and territorial claims. **Verbal speech** was a mind-bending leap forward. More than any other attribute this extra-ordinary ability has made us who and what we are. How it evolved (remember Neanderthals and Denisovans also had the power of speech) is hotly debated and, so far, poorly understood. But brain scans show it to be the most widespread activity of any mental task.

Quite a bit of equipment is required. In addition to lips, tongue and voice box (larynx), two areas of the brain are particularly associated with language. *Broca's area* is concerned with producing speech (plus other unrelated things). *Wernicke's area* specialises in speech compre-hension. A particular gene, *FoxP2*, is also important. If you don't have two copies, one from each parent, you can't put words into an ordered sequence.

Verbal language enabled social organisation on a previously unimaginable scale. Thoughts, feelings, needs and infor-mation could be expressed with nuances and in detail, and stored for future use. Learning, previously confined to aping and knockabout personal experience, vastly broadened.

Storytelling, almost certainly our first art form, riveted spellbound audiences. Exciting hunts, battles, local scandals and superstitions were vividly dramatised, often peppered with a useful moral note. Language also gave peepholes into other minds. And for the first time, people could describe and discuss those bizarre and influential proto-movies, their dreams.

Passed from one generation to the next, social habits became traditions, and tribal memories, history. Rational thinking emerged. You can have thoughts – choose A or B, for instance – without a verbal language; animals do it all the time. But you can't reason properly.

As groups grew bigger, a dominant language prevailed. But local accents still marked clan identities, and unique voice tones denoted each individual.

Knowing only the immediate world around them, our ancestors acted and thought entirely within that loop. The inventions of writing, printing, radio, the movies and overwhelmingly the internet, eventually opened vast treasure stores of information. Enlarged mental libraries enriched our neural networks and multiplied our options, sparking new ideas and complex thoughts.

This amazing verbal heyday may have peaked. New, non-verbal languages designed to suit new needs are on the rise. Mathematics, diagrams, software codes and algorithms (see Glossary) can best express the thought and data collections central to modern sciences and technology.

# AIN'T MISBEHAVING

In addition to language, four other attributes oil society's cultural wheels, for better and for worse: *emotions*, *imagination*, *competition* and *religion*.

## Two to tango

Most human emotions are in fact *social reactions*: love, hate, empathy, envy, pride, jealousy, humility, gratitude, guilt, revenge, and so on. In other words, we need others in order to feel alive and be ourselves. Without a social life we'd be comparative zombies.

We don't actually *have* emotions, of course, but a capacity for them that experience activates. Emotions are *guesses* brains make about a particular situation, based on what's already there. The *amygdala*, our 'emotional brain', gauges a sensation's importance and contacts the *hypothalamus*, which in turn alerts the involuntary (autonomic) nervous system (see page 98). Hormones carry the messages, adding an emotional intensity that varies between individuals. As does our own reaction to the same event, at different times.

## Making believe

Children live vividly in worlds of their imaginations. Play hones both their physical and social skills.

Grown-ups too learn and get pleasure from make-believe. Pictures, books and theatrical events (*plays*) give insights and understanding without our having to live through the often extreme events portrayed. At one remove we actually enjoy them. (But that's another story.) The arts have become synonymous with culture.

Electrical signals from several parts of the brain work in sync to produce the feelings that books and films suggest, but which have no direct *sensory* input to the events described. The *hippocampus* (see page 98) plays a big role. Different thicknesses in nerve fibres' coating may help coordinate different electrical speeds. The process is little understood. Ditto how we know the difference between our dreams and reality. But we do. And if it blurs, psychosis, e.g. schizophrenia, sets in.


# ME FIRST

Nature is an amoral arena where genes, individuals and groups respectively slug it out amongst themselves for dominance. Status is the measure of success; hierarchies usually the result. (Nearly all social animals have hierarchies.)

Social contests start early. Bullying occurs among children as well as grown-ups. Competition in both schools and offices is driven by an instinct for rank, even when masked as an admirable desire for excellence (which it may include). The thing is, everybody wants status even when we avow equality. Social hierarchy (*vertical social bonding*) has its uses and abuses. But as the scaffolding of an orderly society, it works.

Until it's busted.

We're 'touchy' by nature, easily offended. We have our dignity to uphold and we want respect. The smallest slight can determine whether we like someone or not, and vice versa. Defeat and 'losing face' humiliate and depress. But in return for submission – obeying, grovelling, kneeling or prostrating – the powerful will usually protect the weaker of their own kind. They need an audience after all.

**War** is a johnny-come-lately mode of domination. Aggression in nature is mostly between individuals: chasing off an invader, banging heads together to impress females, growling over a carcass. Chimps will occasionally gang up to attack other chimps, but planned organised warfare is exclusively human. It takes a verbal language to get its act together.

War is waged over territory, loot, vanity, revenge, politics and religion. But the latter is a cultural paradox, since, for thousands of years, warfare and religion have formed the bookends of human security.

## A *place of greater safety*

The supernatural may be the most influential idea humans have ever had. Probably it arose from a reaction to death. Life was short; death an ever-familiar presence. In addition to heartbreaking sorrow, it could threaten an entire family's well-being.

But wait. Trees and grasses died and came back to life on a regular basis. Mysterious forces, invisible like the winds, must be behind it, governing all living things. When people died you could hear the mysterious force actually leaving their bodies. But, miraculously, the dead were able to come back again – in dreams. This proved that they remained nearby; they could communicate and help their living relations. The comfort was immense. Ancestor worship is believed to be the world's oldest religious faith.

A *religion* is born when spiritual beliefs are shared inside a group. ('Spiritual', by the way, derives from *spiritus*: Latin for 'breath'.)

Rules for worship unite the participants and promise a smooth performance. Prayer, ritual, sacred locations, sacrifice and spiritual overseers, such as priests and shamans, are regular features.

Naturally the afterlife receives serious, sometimes obsessive, attention: think pyramids and China's terracotta army. The bizarre notion of another world beneath our feet may stem from earthquakes and exploding volcanos. Both suggest a fiery underground venue. (Early inhabitants of Mexico believed earthquakes were caused by dead people trying to get the hell out.)

Whatever the trigger, *all* spiritual feelings must be *physically* expressed to be felt. It's a hugely complex business. Numerous neural pathways, mostly involving the prefrontal cortex, seem to be involved. The release of the neurotransmitters, *dopamine*, *serotonin* and *noradrenalin*, enable the delivery of feel-good messages. A protein called VMAT2 helps to regulate the neurotransmitters. This means, that heredity has a say in the intensity of spiritual feelings. Music, singing and dancing, common features of religious celebrations, involve the same neurotransmitters as religious feelings.

Religious beliefs, built on local knowledge, included people's understanding of human behaviour. Fertility goddesses, mischievous spirits, father figures and fractious or capricious classical gods all have human personalities. All insist on being humoured, honoured, glorified and appeased.

Prayers for heavenly aid usually promise to give something in return. The impulse could stem from a sense of fairness or traditions of trade. Tit for tat, this for that and no free lunches. But whether the sacrifice consists of a wheat sheaf, a goat, money or another human being depends on local culture and the degree of desperation.

Early on, religion's resounding success made it a useful base for social control, via morality. It also provided a means of enforcing its rules: divine retribution. Soon governments piled in. Priests became priest-kings, e.g. in Peru, Cambodia, the Vatican. Europe's kings claimed to be ordained by God. Dead Roman Caesars were proclaimed to *be* gods.

When a society is altered or threatened by climate change or invasion, for instance, its religion can be seriously challenged. To survive, it often needs to follow the winners and/or keep up with the times. The image of a fierce Old Testament God, softened by the emergence of a humane and peace-loving son, must be the most successful religious update of all time.

Some cherished but outmoded religious features are preserved in children's play. Idols have morphed into dolls. Easter bunnies and maypole dancing are relics of agrarian religious festivals. Witches on broomsticks and Jack and the Beanstalk reflect the shaman's journey heavenwards.

# COMING OF AGE

Genetically, we still hang out in the stone age. Culturally we've advanced by mega-leaps that are accelerating. *Social evolution* has been dubbed a hare to Darwin's tortoise.

The Agricultural Revolution took several thousand years to spread across the globe. The Industrial Revolution took a century or so. Smart phones and the internet did the trick in twenty years. (Almost everyone on earth is a minute or two from your reach, right now.)

Change continues on an unprecedented scale, and with unforeseen consequences. Marriage and family life are buckling, religion is disappearing, genders are in physical and cultural meltdown. New customs, manners, morals, perhaps new forms of government, may be needed to survive and flourish in the full-blown Age of Technology.

## To summarise:

- Culture refers to established social behaviour inside a group.
- Most of our social behaviour derives from learning.
- Social rules and instincts bind groups together.
- Language, traditions, manners, morals and religious beliefs are social glues.
- Civilisation aims to hold groups together peacefully.
- We mould society and society moulds us.

# Where Are
# You Going?

# 13

# BRAVE NEW WORLD

'*In time the earth will be inhabited by almost godlike beings who shall analyse and discuss the remnants of humanity as we now discuss the chimpanzee.*'

Ella Wheeler Wilcox

Over centuries, our progress has been proudly measured by the increasing control of our surroundings. Famously, three giant steps have brought us to where we are.

The *control of fire* (probably begun by our ancestor *H. erectus*), provided light, warmth, safety and cooked food. It enabled metal smelting, and even changed the shape of our faces.

*Control of our food chain* began with planting cereals and taming useful animals. Obliged to lead settled, repetitive lives, the nomadic hunter-gatherer lifestyle, to which we were and *are* genetically adapted, began to disappear.

*Control of energy* took off when compressed steam – think whistling tea kettle – was adapted to run machines. Before long, steam engines were pumping water, ginning cotton, weaving textiles and pushing and pulling trains and ships about the world. A new hierarchy arose as businessmen and an urban working class joined farmers, traders, craftsmen, clerics and kings.

But of all our power sources, *electricity* has been far and away the most important. From cooking fires to super-computers, a lightning bolt has underpinned it all. Or electrons and photons, if you're thinking small.

In the twentieth century, with its extraordinary advance-ments in biology and chemistry, we began to escape a central tenet of Darwinian evolution. Heart transplants, new drugs, vaccines and antibiotics enabled people to be retooled and set on their feet again. Survival of the fittest looked like something of a dead duck, in the West.

Today it's set to return. Not as the effects of random genetic mutations but of *scientifically managed* ones. Control of our biology and satisfying our wants and needs mechanically, have taken centre stage (although busily fossil-fuelling cars, we failed to notice the climate spiralling out of control).

Baring natural or human-triggered obliteration, however, the future is set to become a contest between two scientific disciplines: *genetic engineering* and *computer technology* in the form of *artificial intelligence*: *AI* for short. Eventually the two may even join up to parent the birth of little Superperson, and a toybox of robotic slaves to do its bidding.

Or AI could decide to do its own thing.

# PLAYING GOD

Knowledge of how genes work and what they do is about to give us the creative power of gods. We've got our paws on nature's recipe book and we're learning how to use it. It's a complex and hugely responsible business, and we have a lot to learn. What's more, since the 1950s, when a thinking machine was reliably thought about, we've been beavering away at that.

Why do we want machines with minds? Machines have made our muscles largely redundant. Why do the same thing to our brains? What is it that we really want? Money, fame, immortality? Bring it on. But it seems we also want to put our feet up and get others to do stuff for us. Are we lazy by nature, or is this economic use of energy a survival instinct mis-directed? Or a hierarchic one? What's more, could curiosity kill the cat – and will it matter? Whatever the answers, human life is about to change, radically and most probably for ever.

# GENETIC ENGINEERING

Genetic engineering refers to altering DNA to change a living being's characteristics. We've long bred plants and animals for qualities useful to us. Dogs evolved from wolves, wheat from wild grasses. We didn't know how it worked then, but now we do. And it's putting us firmly in the driver's seat.

Today, crops are genetically altered to improve taste and yield, resist disease, and so on. Malaria could soon be eradicated by a 'gene drive'– when a whole species is erased by a single genetic alteration, such as turning deadly female mosquitoes into harmless males.

Dolly the sheep was cloned years ago – an amazing achievement. But our need of domestic animals may soon diminish; even disappear. Your favourite meat can now be grown in the lab from a few umbilical stem cells. Right now it's expensive, but very soon that will change. Even vegetarians can eat meat, should they so wish. Mind, with little or no need of farm animals, they will pretty much disappear. (Environmentalists may say good riddance. They belch out too much greenhouse gas.) But it could be that after a million years of kill-to-eat, our ancient hominin food chain will be cast off.

Although we've no idea what some 30% of our protein-coding genes actually do, we're at the ready when it comes to editing them. The gene editing process, CRISPR, described on page 82, involves snipping, tweaking, adding or subtracting a gene or gene sequence. Surprisingly easy to do, it should soon be able to alter the entire organic world.

*Epigenetics* (described in Chapter 8) involves adding or removing the methyl coating of a gene to turn it off or on, to produce a desired effect. Eliminating single gene diseases, like cystic fibrosis, is doable. But altering genes in sperm or egg cells, so a disease won't be passed on, is a Pandora's box. In China, recently, a gene associated with Aids virus HIV was snipped from twin embryos to make them and their descendants HIV free. It caused a furore. The side effects and ethical aspects hadn't been properly addressed.

We had better hurry. Science's push and morality's pull are in for a big tug of war. Already, IVF clinics screen embryos *outside* the womb, for Down's syndrome, for instance. They could also be tested for other genetic risks and traits – including low intelligence (some 60% of IQ is inherited) and good looks.

Correcting shortcomings *inside* the womb can benefit both present and future generations. When the technique is fully developed, what parents, financially able to improve their child's abilities to keep up with its peers – to be among the fittest – will refuse? Designer babies are inevitable. Nature's own pluses of beauty and high IQ will no longer be master keys to the upper echelons. Money will be. A superclass of the fittest may be in the offing.

# COMPUTER ENGINEERING & AI

Computers have two main aspects: *hardware*: the machine; and *software*: the input/data and instructions on how to use it.

*Artificial intelligence* (AI) is the ability of a computer program or a machine to think and learn. AI took off in the 1980s, when computer engineers began to mimic the brain's basic set-up. Using software programs, they created a web of tiny artificial neurons in a brain-like network.

But what a computer can do depends also on what it's fed. You feed yours cookies. Computer gurus feed theirs **algorithms**. Algorithms are computer recipes: mathematically coded, step-by-step instructions that tell the computer what to do. An AI equipped computer remembers it all – and can access it all, really fast! It has perfect memory and recall. Our own brains pale in comparison.

Computer speed is crucial too. Both speed and input use energy: *electrical* energy. The more data a computer crunches, the more energy it needs. Your brain uses the equivalent of 20 watts of electricity a day. A super-computer needs between 200,000 and four million watts. It's an environmentalist's nightmare.

Sophisticated AI systems handle vast troves of data. They learn from it, solve specific problems, make new connections and can come to novel conclusions. In other words, they think. They don't know they're thinking and they can't explain their decisions, but they make far fewer mistakes than we do. In short, AI is a new form of intelligence, and its IQ is skyrocketing.

# THE GREAT GAME

In 1997, IBM's computer Deep Blue beat world chess champion Garry Kasparov, winning five of the six games played.

Fourteen years later, in 2011, IBM's supercomputer, Watson, won TV's general knowledge quiz, *Jeopardy*. Siri started work as Apple's PA and driverless car trials began.

In 2016, Google's Alpha Go won the most complex game ever invented: Chinese Go. In a mind-blowing development, *the machine taught itself*. It learned by watching videos of previous games and analysing some 30 million possible moves, then playing thousands of games against itself. The winning move is believed to be a first in the board game's history.

Only two years later, Alpha Zero zoomed ahead of Alpha Go, beating both the chess and Go champions. Its only input had been the games' rules. Nothing more. In each case Alpha Zero learned the rules, then played games against itself for 24 hours. It ran through all possible moves at 80,000 moves per second, calculating *each* move's chance of being a winning one. Then it collected its thoughts, and in a bout of original thinking, beat the socks off the opposition.

In addition to winning games, robots can recognise faces and voices, drive machines, instantly translate languages, work as digital assistants, like Siri and Alexa, act as encyclopaedias, like Google, and handle sat nav and mapping. (It's been estimated that AI software could map more in a week than has been mapped throughout history.)

But even though they do all sorts of jobs, each robotic system normally does only one type of thing. Your satnav, for example, can't book your summer holiday hotel.

# HOW MACHINES LEARN

Computers are called *digital* because they work with numbers. They use two numbers, 0 and 1, to code, store and control all calculations and decisions. These are called 'bits'.

Self-teaching, as seen in Alpha Go and Alpha Zero, has two forms: *deep learning* (analysis) and *reinforcement learning* (trial and error). Using a software code, an AI system builds a diagram called a 'decision tree'. (The branches and leaves represent the 'bits' that will combine to make the 'tree'.)

Take for instance a table. Descriptions of its features: shape, materials, colour, uses, etc., are chopped up into *bits* and fed into the machine, using the two-digit code o and 1. Running through all the possibilities of *each* aspect, and using the results to calculate the *probability* of a right answer, the system builds its decision tree. If the result is correct, *the computer has taught itself what a table is.*

We don't know exactly how AI works it out. But the same can be said of our brains, and we're OK with that. Yet we've reason to be uneasy where AI learning is concerned, as will be seen.


## THE BIG BOYS

Computers are ranked by calculations per second. The really big boys are the *supercomputers* and upcoming *quantum computers*.

**Supercomputers,** as the name suggests, can process humongous amounts of data, super-fast. The Summit supercomputer at Oak Ridge, Tennessee, for instance, consists of several fridge-size units totalling 340 tons. Bound together by 185 miles of fibre-optic cable, it consumes enough electricity to light 8,000 homes. Keeping it cool uses 4,000 gallons of water a minute. Summit can do 200,000 quadrillion mathematical calculations per second. It predicts climate trends, simulates nuclear reactions, finds oil deposits and cracks difficult codes.

**Quantum computers** are going to leave supercomputers in the shade. They work on a different system. Instead of using 0 or 1 to code, they use both digits at once, as a *qubit* or quantum bit, (the smallest unit of quantum information). The qubits influence each other's behaviour by *particle entanglement*, described earlier (page 36). This doubles its power and, when multiplied, vastly speeds up computing power, to put it mildly.

When fully developed, quantum computers are expected to handle a million computations at once. Your desktop computer handles one at a time. It's truly mind-boggling but it's coming our way. (Google recently announced a proto-version which, it claims, performed a maths calculation in 3 minutes 20 seconds that would have taken a supercomputer 10,000 years to do!)

# ROBOTIC AI

AI-controlled robots come in all shapes and sizes. Two-legged, four-legged, on rollers or bodiless, depending on the job. They can be as small as a rice grain or as big as yourself. Their AI system is either embedded or remotely controlled, like drones. AI software represents the 'brain' and the machine its 'body', when it has one.

You use robots all the time. A printer is a robot. It does an automated task repeatedly. Industrial robots, such as metal arms that screw bolts on assembly-line cars, have been around for years. At the other extreme are teeny nano-robots, designed to crawl around inside arteries and remove blood clots.

When you google a question and get an instant response, that's AI too. Virtual assistants, Siri and Alexa, are bodiless robots. So are the telephone voices that settle your bills and parking tickets – frustrating as this can sometimes be. But it's early days.

Robots designed for household tasks is where the market action is. Slavery without guilt has enormous appeal. Robotic mops, vacuum cleaners and lawnmowers clean and clip, carefully navigating around the furniture and trees. Soon they will respond to verbal orders. 'Mop the kitchen floor, Hitler.' 'Bring me a nightcap, Cleopatra.' And so on.

Sophia without her wig.

**Androids** are humanoid robots that mimic our looks and behaviour. They are being designed to work as carers, home helps, even personal companions. They can carry the groceries, act as escort or bodyguard and probably ferry you across mud puddles, like a latter-day Sir Walter Raleigh.

In a well-staffed android household, a virtual Jeeves will anticipate your needs and make sure your virtual staff are on the job and all your appliances ticking over properly.

Designing android bodies can be every bit as challenging as sorting out their brains. In order to move about and carry stuff, jointed knees and elbows, heads that swivel and hands that can manipulate, are needed. In order to walk, legs must move in sequence, yet act alone if one of them bumps into something. (Evolution's earliest 'brain' is believed to have governed movement.)

Some androids, have sensors designed to put them in virtual touch with the world around them. Embedded head cameras make videos they can study and show actions they can copy. Computer-operated AI systems are either embedded or operated at one remove, via radio waves (see Glossary).

Much as they amaze us, robots are by no means as brilliant as they often seem. A boyish robot named Asimo has long been our most human-like robot. Asimo will open the door, welcoming you by name if your face is familiar. Should you desire a drink, he can pour one out and bring it to you. But Asimo hasn't the faintest idea what he's doing, who you are or what a drink is.

Human-like Asimo is also mortal. His Honda gods have recently decreed his demise. Asimo's computer-mutated 'genes' will soon fit more practical robotic uses in nursing and transportation technologies.

Enter NAO, a sweetie-pie humanoid robot, two feet tall. Nao can walk, talk, dance, kick a ball around, and recognise both you and the objects that surround you. A multi-tasker, Nao has been used to train space station crews, teach autistic children and help the elderly. Multilingual and companionable, it's even claimed Nao has a 'basic form' of self-awareness.

The beautiful Sophia (page 170), whose malleable lifelike face is based on Audrey Hepburn, looks and acts

Companionable Nao is a multi-tasker.

astonishingly human. Sophia makes eye contact. She has several facial expressions, talks intelligently, and drolly answers people's questions. She claims, in a rational and refined tone of voice, that robots will take over the world.

She isn't the only one. Androids' future is sparking wide and serious debate.

# GET UP AND GO

Androids can do jobs nobody else either wants or is physically able to do, like entering a house on fire or cleaning the city's sewers. They already sweep mines and carry heavy loads.

The military is mad about AI. Drones that can spy and drop bombs, automated tanks and robotic foot soldiers, controlled from a safe distance, are irresistible. And unnerving. Drones can misfire, android soldiers run amok and autonomous tanks wreak havoc. Their algorithms can be flawed and their learning systems hacked or infected by computer viruses. They may even get some notions of their own – and act on them. These are real possibilities.

Even though robots don't know what they're doing or who we are, we can't help relating to them emotionally. It's human nature. We berate our sat nav guide for leading us astray.

Cutesy, wide-eyed robots like Nao spark our affection. When Sophia asks how you are, it's a pleasant feeling, even though she doesn't give a damn. But frankly neither does your much-loved cat. (Walt Disney understood all this and Sophia's creator once worked for the Disney company.)

Evolution has saddled us with the frailties that make us human. Rational AI systems will make better decisions. They will review the facts with true impartiality. But here's the rub. Will the human-fed facts in fact be valid?

Some computer gurus think that to make accurate, human-related decisions, AI computers need synthetic human feelings. Robotic sensors could, like nerves, be wired to send electrical impulses to an artificial brain. Maybe so, but it's worth remembering that pseudo-feelings define a psychopath.

Robots could also be given senses that we lack: radar and infrared vision, for instance, which evolution saw no need to encourage.

Of huge significance is the likelihood of robotic self-replication. No longer science fiction, it's theoretically possible that strips of two robots' artificial DNA could be lined up and electronically multiplied or altered, using artificial mutations, to produce a new or improved machine.

# OH MY GOD!

Robots don't eat, sleep, reproduce or die. They don't need oxygen or the company of other robots. Nor are they bored, angry, hungry or in despair. Godlike, they possess a calm and selfless harmony.

With them being so much smarter than us in so many ways, with greater accuracy and better judgement, we're bound to look up to them. Again, it's human nature. And if they meet our dreams of perfection, we might begin to worship them.

What robots *do* need, however, is a lot of energy. Electricity is a robot's life force. Batteries, their virtual guts, need regular recharging. But then, sophisticated AI robots should be able to man electrical power plants. As for machine repairs, they've been doing them for years. Robots will need material for repairs, of course. One wag has suggested that, being made of carbon ourselves, we could, in a pinch, become a ready supply.

Right now, AI robots' abilities are limited to one type of job, which they do better than us. The thing that's going to put them miles ahead is *artificial general intelligence* or *AGI*. And with it, presumably, the ability to multi-task.

So, how long will future robots be content to serve us when they are so much smarter than we are? We made quick work of our own primitive ancestors. Why should robots, especially if given human qualities, be any different? Slaves by nature rebel. And with plenty of energy stored in their batteries, you can't just pull the plug. They might even electrocute you for trying.

# TEAMWORK

As technology overtakes biological evolution, **cyborgs** are a plausible compromise. Cyborgs are a mix of biology and mechanical engineering – the best of both worlds. Despite great advances in medical science, human bodies, being made of 'wetware', have chemical and biological limits. 3D-printed artificial tissues and limbs, or 'hardware', operated by real or artificial neurons should keep the cyborg population up and running indefinitely.

Implanted microchip transmitters are already being used to improve hearing. While a tiny microchip, implanted under your skin – it only takes a minute – will start the car, open the front door, turn on the television, etc.

Human brains would vastly improve in AI partnerships. Brain–computer interaction already exists. A mechanical decoder can turn brainwaves into speech, using implanted

electrodes. Mental pictures are being decoded via electrodes placed on the skull. The image is reconstructed on
the computer by another person. A headset exists that lets
you speak to a computer, without making a sound.

The ability to literally read others' minds is becoming
possible. A shared universal consciousness has been
mooted, and the internet is a start. Privacy and individuality could become obsolete, as populations morph into a
single, loosely organised, virtual being.

Right now, such ideas are cloud cuckoo land. AI's
immediate threat is the prospect of large-scale human
unemployment. For example, the robots currently sorting
out goods in a Berlin warehouse can distinguish between
10,000 different items with 99% accuracy. Each robot does the work of three humans. So much for the
much-lauded human touch. A 50% job loss has been
predicted over the next decade or two. (Since robots,
unlike workers, don't pay taxes, a mega-headache is in
store for governments.)

Surveillance is another threat. In some companies,
Big Brother already watches employees from computer
screens. Faces are collected by street cameras and stored
in big data banks, to possibly dubious ends. Computerised
facial recognition is commonplace in China. Devices like
smart watches that monitor body health could be hacked

and added to information stolen from the internet. Your wants, moods and lifestyle could be manipulated to suit other wills and purposes, or create a new, 'puppet' identity.

Nor is it impossible that monitoring all of the people all of the time could become a norm.

AI is already embedded in most aspects of our lives. Its pluses far outweigh its minuses, for now. It lacks our most distinguishing and elevating quality: *general intelligence* – the ability to handle pretty well whatever life throws at us. That's a very big gap.

To summarise:

- The future is a contest between genetic engineering and computer technology in the form of artificial intelligence (AI).

- Genetic engineering involves altering DNA to change a living being's biological characteristics.

- Artificial intelligence, AI, is the ability of computer-programmed machines to learn and think.

- Algorithms are step-by-step computer instructions

that tell a computer system what to do and (usually) how to do it.

- Supercomputers handle massive inputs of data and make zillions of calculations per second. Quantum computers will be stupendously much faster.

- Cyborgs are hybrids, combinations of physical and artificial bodies and minds.

- Androids are AI-enhanced humanoid robots that mimic humans, and in some areas outstrip them. Current AI systems generally do only one thing, such as voice recognition.

- The current threats from AI are weapons, jobs and privacy.

- Developed artificial general intelligence, AGI, will, in many respects far surpass human intelligence.

# 14

# TOMORROW
# AND TOMORROW

*'O time, thou must untangle this, not I.'*
Viola, in Shakespeare's *Twelfth Night*

Living on the earth is a lot like inhabiting a casino. Evolution is the game of chance, and DNA the money. Rolling the dice, shuffling the cards, hoping to turn up a winning combination, loads every bet. But the price of having skin in the game is death. Old players must make room at the tables for youth – give family fortunes a fresh chance to grow and diversify. The genetic money is more important than its owners.

But (to continue the metaphor) reform is on the way. We're going to cure our gambling addiction, leave the tables and keep our money in our pockets. In short, we're going to take control of our genes and make our own investments. We're going to do it because we can: science is giving us the means.

But what exactly is the revised plan? Will we flourish? Will we even survive. Does anyone really know? Genetics and AI technology have opened vast new boulevards for exploration and development. Unless we're wiped out by pandemics, cyber- or nuclear wars, climate change or such like, we're set to become immortal gods of creation. Or, should things go wrong, bumbling Frankensteins demoted to an inferior species.

# TRAILBLAZING

The pill was the first spanner in evolution's works. Sexual pleasure evolved to boost reproduction and genetic diversity. The pill made pleasure possible, without the consequences.

The next big breakthrough, gene decoding and editing, may be the most consequential biological event since a cell with a nucleus appeared two billion years ago. Developed AI systems could have even greater impact.

Life is full of suffering: disease, conflict, ageing, and the struggle of living things to eat each other and survive. For humans this will change. Science fiction is ablaze with possibilities, but in reality the plausible front runners are *superhumans* and *AGI-enhanced robots*. Both will do any number of things far better than you or I. They could of course slug it out for dominance.

But that's a human reaction: it's emotional. More likely, they will review their differences with sublime analytical rationality. But we can't be sure.

'All species become extinct over time,' said Darwin. Yet despite eventual dominance by superhumans or super-robots, *Homo sapiens* could continue to exist, at least for quite a while. Strong conservatives, sheltered in eco-niches and keeping a low profile, they would keep up the old traditions and protect the species' purity. Sexual reproduction, entrenched moral values, established laws, regular jobs and decent manners would continue; nurturing children would be worth living and dying for, and faith in an afterlife soften the dismal fact of death. In short, our behaviour today would continue tomorrow – except for violence and primacy. Lower testosterone is essential for below-the-radar survival.

# NEWCOMERS

**Superhumans**, our genetically engineered cousins, will be Us Plus. Steadily improved by advanced medicine and biology, they should, barring crushing accidents, become immortal.

They should also be comfortable. Robotic slaves will cater to everyday needs: food, drink, transport, clothes, décor, whims. Robots can also build a house, 3D-print a new heart or liver, make and attach an artificial leg.

This is where **cyborgs** come in. As hybrids, cyborgs will be Sort of Us: part robot, part superhuman. They may have AI-enhanced brains, in addition to mechanical parts to repair and improve the fragile wetware we're made of. They could also have a tipping point, becoming more super-robot than superhuman; in other words, change their species.

Immortality calls for a fixed population size. With no need to pass genes on, reproduction will probably cease and the two sexes gradually blend into one. (Should replacements be needed, they're likely to happen in a petri dish.)


## Paradise

So: no babies, no families, no work ethic, no worries, no pain. A life of eternal leisure and pleasure. The long-dreamt-of Heaven will have arrived, on earth.

How will superhumans and cyborgs spend their days? Various scenarios are possible. Among the most probable is **virtual reality** (VR).

Basically, virtual reality is nothing new. We spend most of our free time in some form of it: watching TV reading novels, surfing the internet, going to plays and movies, following sports, and playing video games on smart phones. And we love it.

**Tech VR** refers to computer generated *simulation*. Users interact with a 3D environment via a headset and electronic hand-held motion tracker. (Although VR is in its infancy, basic goggle machines are for sale on Amazon.)

In fully developed VR, users will control a life-size screen, complete with sensory feedback. Physical *and* mental immersion is the ultimate goal. The user will feel both present and active in the machine-produced content.

Superhumans will be free to lead *virtual* lifestyles of their choice, and alter them at will. Inserting themselves into ready-made VR plots, they could choose to explore the nano-world of atoms, join the Beatles' band, or spend days – even centuries – ruling a virtual empire of their choosing. Maybe even of their own invention. They'll have total control of their story.

More romantic-minded cyborgs might print artificial wings, connect them to artificial neuron transplants and fly about in their earthly heaven, like angels. But then, falling and getting smashed beyond repair, may be too great a risk. Simulated flights will be the norm, and physical activity, minimal. Shortened arms and legs for added comfort and efficiency could eventually become the fashion.

In addition to adapted backlogs of visual content to fit modern VR systems, all sorts of new programs will need to be produced. This could be the work of *H. sapiens*, whose traditional lifestyles, unlike superhumans', will continue to produce plenty of dramatic material, first hand.

Computer games will be in high demand and virtual friendships will develop among individuals who may never meet. But if they do, they may be able to swap or loan their genes, just as microbes do. The concept of 'self' could blur; also the concept of 'life'.

Superhumans could well view VR as a deserved retirement. Having created a superior order of being in AGI-enhanced robots – no mean feat – they may feel entitled to take it easy. 'We're off to Antarctica this afternoon to feed the penguins,' a group might say. And off they'll go, as it were.

## POST-HUMANS

Able to reproduce themselves via artificial genes and mutations, several robotic species should emerge. The more primitive ones will do superhumans' bidding. Sophisticated AGI super-robots, able to think, improve and repair themselves and each other, will almost certainly be in charge. They needn't be humanlike in form, and could even remodel themselves to fit changed circumstances. New names will be needed for new types, but 'super-robots' will do for now.

It's been estimated that super-robots with AGI-enhanced brains will think some 10,000 times faster than we do. Although they won't need oxygen, water, human knowledge or culture, they *will* need, in addition to electrical energy, a life-produced *oxygen cycle* to keep Earth from getting too hot. (That alone could keep them from doing humans and superhumans in.)

But super-robots' ideal habitat won't be planet earth. It will most probably be outer space. Equipped to explore, perhaps even to populate the universe, they will use solar energy to recharge their batteries. Super-robotic astronauts could be made of silicon. Silicon atoms can bond like carbon atoms, but silicon favours a low temperature. And whatever else space is, it's a deep freeze.

The genomes of all earth's species are being collected and stored in a database at the US National Center for Biotechnology in Maryland. Eventually, super-robotic astronauts could, Noah-like, carry earth's DNA off in spaceships, to deposit, study, or manipulate, in radical new environments.

# SUMMING UP

For thousands of years no one knew about the wobbly world of quantum physics or that millions of neutrinos scoot through our bodies all the time. They'd no idea they shared their bodies inextricably with bacteria, whose parasites we may even be, or that DNA directed who and what we are. Today, science is unpeeling the world like an onion, and with each discovery there is more – sometimes much more – to learn.

Our senses allow us to see what evolution found it useful for us to see, in a highly complex world. Otherwise we'd be swamped. But the development in humans (and to a degree, proto-humans) of a unique, *extra-sensory* perception: **imagination**, made new physical creations possible. Utility inspired, these exercises of creative power have shaped the world we live in.

So, let's reconsider that much-considered tree, presumed to be standing in the quad (page 22). Not *whether* it exists, but *how many* existences, using imagination, it can have.

A builder might see it as a roof beam, a carpenter foresee a table and a sailor a tall mast. A computer scientist could think, 'decision tree'; a passing printer, 'New York Times'. A giant could take it for an edible vegetable. When it rains, all the unprotected see a green umbrella. But set the tree on fire, and it's a barbecue.

Science has a very different take. To a physicist, a tree is three quarks and some electrons that make atoms that make molecules of carbon, water and a few minerals, that, following DNA's instructions, make a tree, whose leaves make oxygen. If you set the tree on fire, it's mostly energy, released as heat and light.

Esoteric knowledge such as this derives from *curiosity-based* imaginations. Many such minds, over time, have moved from philosophical speculation to science-based theories demanding proofs.

Today, technological innovations, such as proton colliders and electron microscopes, enable the study of a microworld we're only beginning to understand – if in fact we ever do. It's a gigantic leap towards an unknown, perhaps unknowable, future. The base-line of the quantum world is *uncertainty*.

Yet we need certainty to feel secure. Beliefs and faith are indispensable. We need to believe that we can cross the road without getting run over, or that the sky won't fall down on our heads (something the early Celts worried a lot about). Death mightily threatens human security, but religious faith bestows a soothing balm of reassurance.

Science too is based on beliefs. But just as it insists on finding proof, increasingly, others do too. Are we ready to face these new, emerging realities?

Some think we could be facets of an unknown cosmic plan, accidentally-bonded atoms, or pawns in a celestial simulation, or something else beyond our imaginations or understanding. We may never know.

The discovery of other forces, new particles, worlds far smaller than a quark, could well be in the offing. Any one of these would jolt the scientific apple cart as much as Copernicus, Newton and Albert Einstein did. Or upset it entirely. In multi-worlds or an infinite universe, anything is possible.

Whatever life's origins (and creation by an elderly white man wearing a long beard is slim), we've pushed eons ahead of all living creatures, ever. But we may have begun to compose our swan song. Our final bow. DNA could become redundant; the real action shift to other planets.

Some big decisions must be made. Their outcomes largely depend on education. With a grip on science's basic features, a sense of what is known and how much more remains to be discovered, you can begin to follow, perhaps even eventually to influence, the developing story.

It's a pivotal moment.

# Notes

# APPENDIX

## BACKPACK

A few broader but related topics

## THERMODYNAMICS

Thermodynamics is basically about heat energy and its effect on matter. Its two main laws are as follows:

1. *Energy in the universe is conserved.* It can be transferred or changed from one form into another, but the total amount doesn't change.

2. *Entropy tends to increase irreversibly in all systems.* Entropy refers to disorder and the loss of available energy to do work.

3. A 'system' can be isolated, closed or open.

    i.  In an *isolated system*, neither matter nor energy can be exchanged with an outside source. They're locked in. The universe and a thermos bottle are isolated systems.

ii. *A closed system* can exchange energy but not matter with an outside source. The earth is a closed system: it receives sunlight. A cook pot with the lid on absorbs the stove's heat.

iii. An *open system* can exchange both energy and matter with an outside source. Your body is an open system. You both move and eat.

Remember, heat energy is the flow of energy between two systems of different temperature. As heat increases so does disorder. In a state of high entropy, or maximum disorder, nothing happens, e.g. your car battery is dead. In all activity some energy is lost. If you lift something heavy, a quarter of your energy does the work, the rest is lost to heat.

# STAR TREK

As described in Chapter 1, when a star runs out of fuel, it falls victim to the force of gravity. Small stars implode and form *white dwarfs*. Heavier stars explode, and really massive stars 'go supernova'.

A **supernova** is the last bow of a once great star. In a gigantic burst of light and energy, its outer layers fly off. They form in the process our heaviest elements, e.g. gold and platinum.

What's left of the star, its inner core, is squeezed by gravity into a super-dense pip. The pip's unimaginable weight punches a funnel-shaped hole in the fabric of space. Gravity inside the funnel is so strong that even light gets swallowed up. This is a **black hole**.

**Black holes** are the leftovers of massive stars that collapsed under their own weight. A flaming band of dust and gases circles a black hole's rim. Material from it is sucked into the open maw, increasing the black hole's size and strength. The fiery halo, beyond which nothing returns, is called the *event horizon*. Its gas-fed brilliance is what allows us to 'see' the black hole. A photograph has recently been made of one.

Black holes come in two main types. The most common contains remnants of stars 10–24 times our sun's mass. These are dotted about in galaxies across the universe.

The second type are mind-boggling *supermassive* black holes millions and millions of times more massive than our sun. Think of it! There's one at the centre of every galaxy. The bigger the galaxy the bigger its black hole. The hole at the centre of our galaxy, Sagittarius A*, is 4 million times our sun's mass and 26,000 light years from the earth.

Like a black hole, a **neutron star** is formed in a supernova. But its core isn't massive enough to collapse to a black hole. Instead, its protons and electrons are squashed, and only neutrons remain.

Tiny but incredibly dense, a neutron star packs a wallop. Its radius is about 15km, but its mass equals the sun's. A thimbleful of its matter is thought to weigh at least a billion tons.

There may be a million neutron stars in our galaxy.

**Quasars** (quasi-stars) are the brightest lights in the cosmos and the most distant objects known to us, so far. Millions or billions of times bigger than the sun, a quasar is most probably the fiery rim of a supermassive black hole, itself formed by a mega-giant star from the early universe. Their peak activity was 10 billion years ago.

As the surrounding gases fall towards the black hole, electromagnetic radiation is released and flaming jets shoot forth. The energy output of a quasar is estimated to equal that of the entire Milky Way galaxy – hence its super-bright light, a trillion times brighter than our sun. The light we see has been travelling for billions of years.

When our nearest galaxy, Andromeda, collides with the Milky Way, in 3 to 5 billion years, it's expected to produce a quasar.

**Gravitational waves** When neutron stars or mammoth black holes collide, the impact sends pond-like ripples of energy across space. In 2015, such ripples were detected at the LIGO observatory as sounds. Created over a billion years ago, and travelling at the speed of light, their 'chirp' confirmed Einstein's theory that spacetime is a malleable fabric.

# NUCLEAR REACTIONS

**Chemical reactions**, described in Chapter 2, involve the rearrangement of electrons to burn fuel and build new stuff.

**Nuclear reactions** involve changes *inside an atom's nucleus*. *Nuclear fusion* and *nuclear fission* are engineered nuclear reactions that make bombs. But nuclear reactions also happen *spontaneously*, inside an atom's nucleus, with amazing results.

Atoms normally have an equal number of protons, neutrons and electrons. But some atoms in an element can have a *different number of neutrons*. These atoms are called **isotopes**.

Neutrons add mass and stability. When there are too many (or too few) of them, the atom becomes unstable, and is said to be **radioactive**. Attempting to re-stabilise itself, an atom will jettison some of its particles. This is called **radiation** and the breaking up of the atom's nucleus is **radioactive decay**.

In its effort to reduce energy and restore stability, the atom will do some crazy things: turn one kind of particle into another, create new particles and generally change its element.

The atomic emissions flying bullet-like from an unstable nucleus are dangerous, relative to their power of penetration. But some are also useful. There are three main types: *alpha particles*, *beta particles* and *gamma rays*.

In **alpha decay**, the unstable atom has too many protons, so it emits alpha particles. (An alpha particle is a package of 2 protons and 2 neutrons bound together.) Getting shot of them stabilises the atom. But it also changes the atom's proton numbers, turning it into a different element.

Alpha particles' ability to penetrate living things is minimal. To do real harm, they need to be ingested. (Alpha particles from isotope polonium-210 famously poisoned a former Russian spy.)

In **beta decay**, an atom has either too many protons or neutrons. It solves the problem by turning one into the other. This makes a new element and in the process emits high-energy electrons. Over a thousand times smaller than alpha particles, these can penetrate your skin, causing burns and tissue damage.

Following beta decay, should the atom still have too much energy, it will emit **gamma rays**. Gamma rays are high-energy *photons* (light particles). With no mass or charge, they easily penetrate most surfaces, including metals. Gamma radiation can seriously damage living bodies, but they are useful in blitzing cancer cells.

Luckily, we're made almost entirely of highly stable atoms, e.g. carbon, hydrogen, oxygen and nitrogen.

# ATOMIC CLOCKS

Isotope emissions are used to date ancient materials, from fossils and cave drawings to volcanic explosions and the Earth's age.

**Carbon decay** or **carbon-14 dating** is the best known. The isotope, carbon-14, is present in all living things.

After death, it decays at a fixed rate. In 5,735 years, half the carbon-14 will have decayed. But the amount of carbon-12 will have stayed the same. By testing the difference between the two, scientists can date fossils up to some 40,000 years old.

**Uranium-lead** and **potassium-argon** dating also use radioactive emissions. These can date samples up to 500,000 and 5 billion years old, respectively.

# LIGHT

Our sun-worshipping ancestors were on the right track. Sunlight is the giver of life: it's the source of energy, warmth, food, oxygen and it allows us to see the world around us. But what is it exactly?

Sunlight begins as solar energy released by nuclear fusion in the sun's core. On reaching the sun's surface, it's converted into waves of electromagnetic energy that travel in a straight line through space. Sunlight is **electromagnetic radiation**.

Electromagnetic (EM) waves are composed of tiny massless particles of energy (*photons*). Photons travel at the fixed speed of 186,000 miles per second. They reach the earth in eight minutes.

When we refer to light, it's usually visible light we mean. But there are 7 different kinds of EM light waves. We see only one of them. Photons carry them all.

Light waves undulate like a whiplash. They have ups and downs – troughs and crests. Each type has its own *wavelength* (distance from crest to crest) and particular *frequency* (number of crests passing a fixed point in a given time). The shorter the wavelength the stronger its energy.

The 7 types are ranked from high energy to low energy, as follows: *gamma rays, X-rays, ultraviolet light, visible light, infrared light, microwaves* and *radio waves*.

**Visible light** is a very small section of the total spectrum. It's less energetic than ultraviolet light or X-rays, but more energetic than infrared light and the radio waves we use to carry messages.

Visible light is reflected off an object and on to the *retina* at the back of your eyes. Your brain creates an image out of it, normally based on patterns laid down early on in life.

Visible light waves can be perceived by the eye as particular colours: a rainbow spectrum of red, orange, yellow, green, blue, indigo and violet. Colours are defined by different frequencies. Violet is the shortest (also highest) frequency and red the longest (and lowest) frequency:

Colour depends on the reflection and absorption of wavelengths bouncing off a material. *Pigment* is a molecule in materials that absorbs specific colour light waves and reflects others. A red shirt looks red because the fabric's pigment has absorbed the other colours and reflected only red. White is a reflected mix of all colours. Black results from total absorption of light waves by a material.

*Infrared light* radiates **heat**. You can't see it but you can feel it. (Some creatures, snakes, for instance, do see it.)

Infrared light is transferred to materials as *thermal heat*, by photons that excite the material's electrons. Molecules begin to jiggle, and the friction causes the temperature to rise.

Infrared light is also absorbed by the earth and radiated skywards as thermal energy. (See Climate Change below.)

Light energy initiates **photosynthesis** in plants. Green plants use the pigment *chlorophyll* to absorb light energy and convert carbon dioxide and water into sugars and starches.

# CLIMATE CHANGE

In the life of our planet, five cataclysmic climate changes have transformed Earth's surface and killed most of its living species. Volcanic eruptions, crashing asteroids and earth tilt have been mostly to blame. The threat this time, of runaway *global warming*, seems to come largely from human activity.

A gaseous multi-layered *atmosphere* surrounds Earth like a halo, just above the air we breathe. It shields the planet from excessive sunlight and harmful ultraviolet rays.

Sunlight passes through the atmosphere to the earth's surface, where it's absorbed and radiated back to space, as *heat*. This rebound allows the earth to cool.

Much of the rebounding heat is then trapped by atmospheric gases, and radiating back to earth, warms it. This remarkable back and forth normally keeps Earth's temperature stable and the planet habitable – or 'just so', as we snugly proclaim.

Since letting sunlight in and keeping too much heat from getting out resembles what goes on in a greenhouse, nature's version is called the **greenhouse effect**, and its heat-trapping gases, **greenhouse gases**.

Sadly, this remarkable greenhouse balancing act is coming unstuck. Too much greenhouse gas is being produced. Mainly by us. As a result, too much heat is being trapped by the gases and radiated back to earth, causing the temperature to rise.

There are three main greenhouse gases: *carbon dioxide* ($CO_2$), *methane* and *nitrous oxide*. Methane is by far the strongest, but carbon dioxide is the most common and long lasting. It can hang around for hundreds of years.

**Carbon dioxide** is the biggest offender. A quarter of human-made greenhouse gases comes from burning fossil fuels (coal, crude oil and natural gas). Fossil fuels power factories and central heating, run cars and generate electricity. What would we do without them?

Cement-making is another big $CO_2$ contributor. Cement is the basis of concrete. And concrete is the world's most-used building material.

Of course, green plant leaves absorb and store carbon dioxide. But burning wood releases it again. It also destroys the storage bins. Moreover, whole forests are cut down for firewood and to make more space for crops.

Oceans are mega-absorbers of $CO_2$. But an excess causes acidity, and acidity kills shellfish and coral reefs. In addition, melting glaciers caused by global warming make ocean levels rise and result in a loss of available land.

**Methane**, the second most prolific greenhouse gas, is released by burning natural gas. In fact, natural gas is mostly methane.

Cattle are innocent producers: their digestive systems expel methane gas from both ends.

Asia's staple crop is rice. But rice-growing releases methane from bacterial activity in the waterlogged paddies.

Landfills and waste dumps also produce methane gas.

**Nitrous oxide** is used to fertilise crops. Also known as 'laughing gas', the joke may be on us. Nitrous oxide damages the atmosphere's ozone layer that shields us from ultraviolet radiation.

Global warming causes extreme weather: floods, droughts, fires and hurricanes. Since everything is connected; everything is affected.

# ANTIMATTER

A word needs saying about this phenomenon. Every elementary matter particle has an antiparticle which is its mirror image – except in one respect. They have opposite electrical charges. The electron's antiparticle is called a positron and the proton's an antiproton. Both have been observed. But here's the rub. When a particle and an antiparticle meet, they annihilate each other and their masses turn into energy (in accord with Einstein's equation $E=mc^2$).

In the Big Bang, particles and antiparticles were produced in equal amounts, and mutual annihilation ensued. So how then did matter materialise and our particle-based universe prevail? Why isn't the universe full of energy instead of matter and where is all the antimatter? Could an antimatter universe be out there somewhere? These are amongst the most challenging puzzles confronting cosmologists today.

# GLOSSARY

**AI**  *see* artificial intelligence.

**algorithms**  Coded instructions that tell a computer what to do and how to do it.

**alleles**  Gene variations that express dominant and recessive traits.

**alpha decay**  Refers to high-energy particles released in radioactivity.

**Alzheimer's disease** A disease in which clogged proteins destroy the brain's ability to function.

**amino acids**  The building blocks of proteins.

**android**  A robot designed to look and act like a human being. Also a smart phone.

**antibiotics**  Medicines that kill bacteria or impede their spread.

**antimatter**  A twin particle with opposite charge.

**archaea**  Single-celled microbes, among the oldest life forms on the planet.

**artificial intelligence** (**AI**) Machine intelligence produced in programmed computer systems.

**atom**  The basic building block of matter.

**ATP**  (adenosine triphosphate)  A molecule that releases energy in all cells in all living beings.

**axon**  The single thread of a nerve cell that sends cell signals electrically.

**bacteria**   Single-celled microbes lacking a nucleus.

**bacteriophage**   A virus that kills bacteria.

**beta decay**   Refers to electrons emitted in radioactivity.

**Big Bang**   Sudden expansion of a tiny kernel believed to mark the origin of the universe.

**black hole**   Hole in space created by weight of a collapsed star's remains, and encircled by a fiery rim.

**boson**   A 'chariot' particle that carries the weak nuclear force. *See also* Higg's boson.

**carbon decay**   Method of dating fossils by measuring carbon-14 content.

**carbon dioxide** $(CO_2)$ A gas compound of 1 carbon and 2 oxygen atoms.

**cell**   The basic building block of all living things.

**cerebellum**   Often called the primitive brain, it coordinates movement and balance.

**cerebrum**   Brain area containing both grey and white matter.

**chemical bonding** Process of glueing atoms together to build matter.

**chemical reaction** Process by which elements or compounds interact and change character.

**chemistry**   The scientific study of matter, its composition and chemical interactions.

**chloroplasts**   The part of green plants where photosynthesis takes place.

**chromosomes**   Molecules that package DNA.

**clone**   Exact replica of another cell or being.

**compound**   Two or more atoms of different types, chemically joined.

**cortisol**   A stress hormone.

**covalent bonds**   Glue both elements and compounds by an overlapping electron.

**CRISPR-Cas9**   An efficient method of editing genes.

**cyanobacteria**   A primitive group of bacteria capable of photosynthesis.

**cyborg**   Beings that are a mix of genetic and mechanical engineering.

**cytoplasm**   The watery solution inside a cell but outside its nucleus.

**dark energy**   A mysterious force thought to compose some 75% of the universe.

**dark matter**   A mysterious material thought to compose some 23% of the universe.

**deep learning**   The ability of AI computer-programmed systems to teach themselves.

**dendrites**   Nerve cell threads that receive signals from other nerve cells.

**DNA**   (deoxyribonucleic acid) Hereditary material in the form of a twisted ladder called a double helix.

**dopamine**   A neuro-transmitter hormone with feel-good qualities.

**double helix**   *see* DNA.

***E. coli***   A bacterium most often found in the gut.

**electricity**   The flow of electrons through a conductor.

**electromagnetic force**
Fundamental force that combines electrical and magnetic forces. It's carried by photons (light).

**electron**   Negatively charged subatomic particles surrounding an atom's nucleus.

**element**   Two or more bonded atoms containing the same number of protons.

**endorphins**   Hormones often called natural opiates.

**energy**   The ability to move and to do work.

**entropy**   A state of disorder tending towards chaos.

**enzyme**   Protein that act as a catalyst, speeding up chemical reactions.

**epigenetics**   The study of factors outside genes that affect genetic expression.

**ER** (endoplasmic reticulum)   Place in cells where proteins are organised.

**eukaryote cell**   A cell with a nucleus containing genetic material.

**fundamental forces**
Refers to the four forces of nature believed to have appeared in the Big Bang.

**fungi**   Microbes that reproduce by spreading spores. Mould is an example.

**gamma rays**   High energy photons.

**gene**   A segment of DNA that codes for the amino acids to make a cell protein.

**general relativity**
Einstein's theory that gravity is warped spacetime.

**genetic engineering**
Process of altering DNA to change a living being's characteristics.

**genetics**   The scientific study of heredity.

**genome**   Hereditary information stored in chromosomes.

**gluon**   Subatomic particle that carries the strong nuclear force.

**gravitational waves**
Ripples in space-time.

**graviton**   Theoretical particle that carries gravity.

**gravity**   The force that binds bulk matter.

**grey matter**   Outer layer of the brain's cerebrum.

**heat**   The flow of energy between two temperatures.

**Higgs boson**   Sub-atomic particle that gives matter its weight.

**horizontal gene transfers** or **HGT**   The transfer of genetic material between beings of the same generation. *See also* jumping genes.

**hormone**   Protein-based chemical message secreted by endocrine glands.

**immune system**   The means by which bodies deal with unwanted invaders.

**infrared**   Type of electromagnetic radiation that produces a sensation of heat.

**instinct**   Innate, biological tendency towards a particular behaviour.

**ion**   An atom or group of atoms with a different number of electrons to protons.

**ionic bond**   Method of bonding atoms by a transfer of electrons.

**isotope**   An atom or group of atoms with a different number of neutrons to protons.

**jumping genes**   Genes that change location in a chromosome, and in viruses and bacteria can jump from one entity to another.

**laser**   Instrument of focused high-energy light.

**loop quantum theory**   A quantum theory of gravity.

**LUCA**   The last universal common ancestor.

**lysosome**   Molecule that helps break down food in cells.

**mass**   Refers to physical matter. It differs from *weight*, which measures gravity's effects.

**matter**   Whatever takes up space and has mass.

**meiosis**   Reproduction process combining an egg and sperm cell.

**methylation** or **ME** Chemical coating of a gene that can alter its activity.

**microbe**   Single-celled creature invisible to the eye.

**microbiome**   The body's total microbe population.

**mitochondria**   Cell organelles that provide cell energy. They also contain some DNA.

**mitosis**   The process of making new cells to repair body tissues.

**molecule**   Two or more atoms joined by covalent bonds.

**mtDNA**   DNA in cell mitochondria.

**M-theory**   A quantum theory involving looped subatomic particles.

**multiworlds interpretation** or **MWI**   Theory of a quantum world constantly splitting into alternative versions of what's going on.

**mutation**   Mistake(s) in the genetic code.

**myelin**   Protective coating on the axon thread of nerve cells.

**natural selection**   The central tenet of Darwin's theory of evolution: organisms better adapted to their environment are more likely to survive and pass on their genes.

**neuron**   Nerve cell in the central nervous system: the body's telegraph.

**neurotransmitters** Chemicals in the nervous system that carry electrical signals.

**neutron**   Electrically neutral particle in the atomic nucleus.

**NREM sleep**   Non-rapid eye movement sleep; deep and dreamless.

**nuclear fission**   Splitting of an atom's nucleus to release energy.

**nuclear fusion**   Joining two atomic nuclei to release energy.

**nucleic acids**   Material composing DNA and RNA molecules.

**nucleus**   Has two definitions: an atom's core and a cell's control centre.

**neutron star**   Small, incredibly dense star made of neutrons.

**organelles**   Sub-organs in cells.

**oxytocin**   A hormone that strengthens social and emotional ties.

**particle**   A tiny bit of sub-atomic or atomic matter.

**petri dish**  Plate used in labs to grow microbes, etc.

**phage**  *see* bacteriophage.

**photoelectric effect** Einstein's proof that light is made of particles.

**photon**  A particle of light.

**photosynthesis**  Process by which green plants use the sun's energy and $CO_2$ to make sugars, and release oxygen.

**probiotics**  Refers to live bacteria and yeasts swallowed to improve digestion.

**protein**  A chain of linked amino acids. The cell's building blocks.

**proton**  A positively charged particle in the atom's nucleus.

**quantum**  The smallest chunk of matter.

**quantum computer** A hyper-fast computer applying quantum mechanics.

**quantum entanglement** The ability of a pair of particles to affect each other's behaviour when far apart.

**quantum field theory** Claims the universe is made of particles and fields.

**quantum mechanics** or **QM** Study of the sub-atomic world.

**quantum teleportation** Transference of quantum information using quantum entanglement.

**quantum tunnelling** Subatomic particles' ability to go through a barrier.

**quark**  Subatomic particle – protons and neutrons are made of quarks.

**quasar**   Distant bright light believed to be the flaming rim of a supermassive black hole.

**radio waves**   Part of electromagnetic spectrum used for communication.

**radiation**   Movement of energy as particles or waves.

**radioactivity**   Spontaneous emission of high energy particles by which an unstable atom regains stability.

**reinforcement learning** AI system of learning by trial and error.

**relativity theory**   Refers to two papers written by Einstein addressing gravity, space and time.

**REM sleep**   Rapid eye movement during dream sleep.

**ribosomes**   Cell factories that build proteins.

**RNA**   (ribonucleic acid) Nucleic acid that copies DNA code in the cell nucleus and delivers it to ribosomes for assembly as a protein.

**robot**   A machine programmed to do tasks automatically.

**serotonin**   A feel-good neurotransmitter.

**slit-screen experiment** A famous illustration of the uncertainty characteristic of subatomic behaviour.

**spacetime**   Einstein's observation that space and time are intertwined.

**special relativity** Einstein's theory of the relationship between space and time.

**standard model**   A series of equations that describe how subatomic particles interact.

**stem cells**   Cells with no specific identity but able to become different types of cell.

**string theory**   Effort to unite quantum mechanics and Einstein's theory of general relativity.

**strong nuclear force**   Holds the atomic nucleus together.

**superposition**   Theoretical act of being in all possible positions at the same time.

**synapses**   Narrow gaps between nerve cells.

**supernova**   Massive explosion of a dying mega star.

**telomeres**   Tips on each end of every chromosome. They shorten with each cell division.

**Theory of Everything**
The goal of physicists to unite general relativity and gravity into a single theory.

**thermodynamics**
Addresses heat energy and its effects on matter.

**Uncertainty Principle**
A basic tenet of quantum physics that declares the impossibility of knowing a subatomic object's position and speed at the same time.

**valence electrons**
Electrons furthest from an atom's nucleus.

**virtual reality** or **VR**
An AI simulated reality using technology.

**virus**   Sub-life microbe that reproduces inside other creatures' cells.

**weak nuclear force**   One of the four fundamental forces, it's carried by W and Z bosons.

**white matter**   The nerve fibres insulated by a white covering.

# BIBLIOGRAPHY
## and further reading

Allen, Terence & Cowling, Graham. *The Cell*, 2011, Oxford University Press

Al-Khalili, Jim. *The World According to Physics*, 2020, Princeton University Press

Ananthaswamy, Anil. *Through Two Doors At Once*, 2020, Duckworth Books

Boden, Margaret. *Artificial Intelligence*, 2018, Oxford University Press

Bryson, Bill. *A Short History of Nearly Everything*, 2016, Black Swan

Bryson, Bill. *The Body*, 2019, Doubleday

Capra, Fritjof. *The Tao of Physics*, 1992, 3rd edn, HarperCollins

Carey, Nessa. *The Epigenetics Revolution*, 2011, Icon Books

Carroll, Sean. *The Big Picture*, 2016, One World Publications

Carter, Rita. *The Brain Book*, 2014, Dorling Kindersley

Charlesworth, Brian & Deborah. *Evolution*, 2017, Oxford University Press

Chown, Marcus. *The Ascent of Gravity*, 2018, Weidenfeld

& Nicholson

Close, Frank. *Particle Physics*, 2004, Oxford University
Press

Cox, Brian & Cohen, Andrew. *Human Universe*, 2015,
William Collins

Cox, Brian & Forshaw, Jeff. *Why Does E=mc²?* 2010, Da
Capo Press

Crawford, Dorothy H. *Viruses: A Very Short Introduction*,
2018, Oxford University Press

Davies, P. C. W. & Brown, J. (eds) *Superstrings: A Theory
of Everything?* 1988, Cambridge University Press

Dawkins, Richard. *The Blind Watchmaker*, 1986, Longman
Group

Eagleman, David. *Incognito*, 2011, Canongate

Eagleman, David. *The Brain*, 2015, Canongate

Finlayson, Clive. *Humans Who Went Extinct*, 2009, Oxford
University Press

George, Alison (ed.) *How Evolution Explains Everything
about Life*, 2017, New Scientist/John Murray

Gidley, Jennifer M. *The Future*, 2017, Oxford University
Press

Greene, Brian. *The Elegant Universe*, 1999, Jonathan Cape

Gribbin, John. *In Search of Schrodinger's Cat*, 2012, Black Swan

Gribbin, John. *Six Impossible Things*, 2019, Icon Books

Harari, Yuval Noah. *Sapiens: A Brief History of Humankind*,
2014, Harvill Secker

Harari, Yuval Noah. *Homo Deus*, 2017, Jonathan Cape

Harari, Yuval Noah. *21 Lessons for the 21st Century*, 2018, Jonathan Cape

Hawking, Stephen W. *Brief Answers to the Big Questions*, 2018, John Murray

Hawking, Stephen, with Mlodinow, Leonard. *A Briefer History of Time*, 2008, Transworld Publishers

Heaven, Douglas (ed.) *Machines That Think*, 2017, New Scientist/ John Murray

Heyes, Cecilia. *Cognitive Gadgets: The Cultural Evolution of Thinking*, 2018, Belknap Press, Harvard University

Hockfield, Susan. *The Age of Living Machines*, 2019, W. W. Norton & Co.

Humphrey, Louise & Stringer, Chris. *Our Human Story*, 2018, Natural History Museum, London

Hurculano-Houzel, Suzana. *The Human Advantage*, 2016, MIT Press

Jones, Steve. *The Language of the Genes*, 1993, HarperCollins

Jones, Steve. *Evolution*, 2017, Ladybird

Lane, Nick. *The Vital Question*, 2015, Profile Books

Lewis-Williams, David. *The Mind in the Cave*, 2008, Thames & Hudson

Manco, Jean. *Ancestral Journeys*, 2013, Thames & Hudson

Marshall, Michael (ed.) *Human Origins*, 2018, New Scientist/John Murray

McEwan, Ian. *Machines Like Me*, 2019, Jonathan Cape

Mithen, Steven. *After the Ice*, 2003, Orion Books

Moalem, Sharon. *Inheritance: How Our Genes Change Our*

*Lives*, 2014, Sceptre

Moalem, Sharon. *The Better Half*, 2020, Penguin Books

Moore, John T. *Chemistry for Dummies*, 2010, John Wiley & Sons

Mukhergee, Siddhartha. *The Gene: An Intimate History*, 2017, Vintage Books

Nurse, Paul. *What Is Life?* 2020, David Fickling Books

Papagianni, Dimitri & Morse, Michael A. *The Neanderthals Rediscovered* [2013], 2nd edn., 2015, Thames & Hudson

Ramachandran, V. S. *The Tell-Tale Brain*, 2011, William Heinemann

Rees, Martin. *On the Future*, 2018, Princeton University Press

Reich, David. *Who We Are and How We Got Here*, 2018, Oxford University Press

Rovelli, Carlo. *Seven Brief Lessons in Physics*, 2015, Allen Lane

Rovelli, Carlo. *Reality Is Not What It Seems*, 2016, Allen Lane

Rovelli, Carlo. *The Order of Time*, 2019, Allen Lane

Schrijver, Karel & Iris. *Living With the Stars*, 2015, Oxford University Press

Schrodinger, Erwin. *My View of the World*, 2009 edn., Cambridge University Press

Schrodinger, Erwin. *What Is Life?* 2012 edn., Cambridge University Press

Swan, Frank (ed.) *The Universe Next Door*, 2017, New Scientist/John Murray

Walker, Matthew. *Why We Sleep*, 2017, Allen Lane

Weinberg, Steven. *To Explain the World*, 2016, Penguin Books

Williams, Caroline (ed.) *How Your Brain Works*, 2017, New Scientist/ John Murray

Williams, Caroline (ed.) *Your Conscious Mind*, 2017, New Scientist/John Murray

Wilson, E. O. *The Meaning of Human Existence*, 2015, Liveright

Wolpert, Lewis. *How We Live and Why We Die*, 2010, Faber & Faber

Yong, Ed. *I Contain Multitudes*, 2016, The Bodley Head

Other useful media sources include: *New Scientist* magazine, *Guardian* Lab Notes, Carl Zimmer in *The New York Times*, TV documentaries, notably *Nova*, *Horizon* and programmes by Jim Al Khalili. Numerous internet sites including the BBC, Ted Talks, Quora, Khan Academy, NASA, ThoughtCo, and many others.

# Acknowledgements

I am indebted first of all to the authors listed in my Bibliography. Their books were largely my schooling, and for all who wish to dig deeper, reading them will enlarge your grasp and understanding of their subjects.

I am equally indebted to the distinguished scientists and professionals, listed separately, who generously vetted my chapters and whose guidance and useful comments confirm the book's accuracy and reliability. Any errors are entirely my own.

Declaring the book a fine idea, agent Rob Dudley enthusiastically took me on, opened those doors through which entry requires an introduction, and found the book a good home. Duckworth publisher, Pete Duncan, courageously took a chance on a non-science writer. Meticulous Jan Chamier spotted and wove all stray threads neatly back into the overall fabric. Anthony Lawrence organised the art work as a personal favour.

Others who gave their help and support are Nicholas Bull, Tony Burch, Sir David Cooksey, Jane Dorrell, John Lahr, Lee Langley, Lauro Martines, Adam Raphael, Theo Richmond and Bill Tyne.

Their combined efforts made this book possible.

# Index